Georgia
Test Prep

Frank Schaffer Publications®

This edition printed in the United States in 2006 by Frank Schaffer Publications expressly for School Box. Frank Schaffer Publications is an imprint of School Specialty Publishing. Copyright © 2006 School Specialty Publishing.

Send all inquiries to:
The School Box
900 Cobb Place Blvd.
Kennesaw, GA 30152

ISBN 0-7682-2755-0

1 2 3 4 5 6 PAT 11 10 09 08 07 06

Table of Contents

What's Inside?

This workbook is designed to help you and your fifth grader understand what he or she will be expected to know on the Georgia fifth-grade state tests.

Practice Pages

The workbook is divided into four sections: English/Language Arts, Mathematics, Social Studies, and Science. Each section has practice activities that have questions similar to those that will appear on the state tests. Students should use a pencil to fill in the correct answers and to complete any writing on these activities.

Georgia State Standards

Before each practice section is a list of the state standards covered by that section. The shaded *What it means* sections will help to explain any information in the standards that might be unfamiliar.

Mini-Tests and Final Tests

Practice activities are grouped by state standard. When each group is completed, the student can move on to a mini-test that covers the material presented on those practice activities. After an entire set of standards and accompanying activities are completed, the student should take the final tests, which incorporates materials from all the practice activities in that section.

Final Test Answer Sheet

The final tests have a separate answer sheet that mimics the style of the answer sheets the students will use on the state tests. The answer sheets appear at the end of each final test.

How Am I Doing?

These pages are designed to help students identify areas where they are proficient and areas where they still need more practice. Students can keep track of each of their mini-test scores on these pages.

Answer Key

Answers to all the practice activities, mini-tests, and final tests are listed by page number and appear at the end of the book.

Frequently Asked Questions

What kinds of information does my child have to know to pass the test?

The Georgia Department of Education provides a list of the knowledge and skills that students are expected to master at each grade level. The activities in this workbook provide students with practice in each of these areas.

Are there special strategies or tips that will help my child do well?

The workbook provides sample questions that have content similar to that on the state tests. Test-taking tips are offered throughout the book.

How do I know what areas my child needs help in?

A special *How Am I Doing?* section will help you and your fifth grader evaluate progress. It will pinpoint areas where more work is needed as well as areas where your student excels.

Georgia English/Language Arts Content Standards

The English/language arts section measures knowledge in four different areas:

1) Reading

2) Writing

3) Conventions

4) Listening, Speaking, and Viewing

Georgia English/Language Arts Table of Contents

Reading Standards

In reading a text closely, the student works carefully to discern the author's perspective and the particular facts and details that support it. The student reads thoughtfully and purposefully, constantly checking for understanding of the author's intent and meaning so that the interpretation will be sound.

ELA5R1. The student demonstrates comprehension and shows evidence of a warranted and responsible explanation of a variety of literary and informational texts. The texts are of the quality and complexity illustrated by the Grade Five Reading List, located on page 35. *(See pages 8–31.)*

<u>For literary texts</u>, the student identifies the characteristics of various genres and produces evidence of reading that:

a. identifies and analyzes the elements of setting, characterization, and conflict in plot.

b. identifies and analyzes the structural elements particular to dramatic literature (e.g., scenes, acts, cast of characters, stage directions) in the plays read, viewed, written, and performed.

c. identifies and analyzes the similarities and differences between a narrative text and its film or play version.

d. relates a literary work to information about its setting (historically or culturally).

e. identifies imagery, figurative language (e.g., personification, metaphor, simile, hyperbole), rhythm, or flow when responding to literature.

What it means:

- **Figurative language** is language used for descriptive effect. It describes or implies meaning, rather than directly stating it. Examples of figurative language include:
  - **personification**—assigning human qualities, feelings, or actions to an animal, an object, or an idea. Example: The mother bear cried for her cub.
  - **metaphor**—comparing unlike things but without using *like* or *as*. Example: His body was a well-oiled machine.
  - **simile**—using *like* or *as* to compare things that may seem unlike each other. Example: Her smile was as dazzling as the sun.
  - **hyperbole**—using exaggeration to convey strong emotion, express humor, or emphasize a point. Example: I felt like we walked a million miles!

f. identifies and analyzes the author's use of dialogue and description.

g. applies knowledge of the concept that theme refers to the main idea and meaning of a selection, whether implied or stated.

h. responds to and analyzes the effects of sound, figurative language, and graphics in order to uncover meaning in poetry.
   i. Sound (e.g., alliteration, onomatopoeia, rhyme scheme)
   ii. Figurative language (e.g., personification, metaphor, simile, hyperbole)
   iii. Graphics (e.g., capital letters, line length)

i. makes judgments and inferences about setting, characters, and events and supports them with elaborating and convincing evidence from the text.

j. identifies similarities and differences between the characters or events and theme in a literary work and the actual experiences in an author's life.

k. identifies common structures and stylistic elements (e.g., hyperbole, refrain, simile) in traditional literature.

Reading Standards

<u>For informational texts</u>, the student reads and comprehends in order to develop understanding and expertise and produces evidence of reading that:

a. locates facts that answer the reader's questions.
b. identifies and uses knowledge of common textual features (e.g., paragraphs, topic sentences, concluding sentences, glossary).
c. identifies and uses knowledge of common graphic features (e.g., charts, maps, diagrams, captions, and illustrations).
d. identifies and uses knowledge of common organizational structures (e.g., chronological order, logical order, cause and effect, classification schemes).
e. distinguishes cause from effect in context.
f. identifies and analyzes main ideas, supporting ideas, and supporting details.
g. makes perceptive and well-developed connections.
h. relates new information to prior knowledge and experience and makes connections to related topics or information.

ELA5R2. The student consistently reads at least twenty-five books or book equivalents (approximately 1,000,000 words) each year. The quality and complexity of the materials to be read are illustrated in the sample reading list, located on page 35. The materials should include traditional and contemporary literature (both fiction and nonfiction) as well as magazines, newspapers, textbooks, and electronic material. Such reading should represent a diverse collection of material from at least three different literary forms and from at least five different writers.

Reading Standards ELA5R3 and ELA5R4 *(See page 34.)*

Analyzing Literary Elements

DIRECTIONS: Read the story and then answer the questions on the next page.

I'll Save You

It was just Dollar Lake, the size of five or six backyards filled with water. "Not much bigger than a kiddie pool," my mom always said. But it was deep and cold. Springs fed the small lake, and it was such a dark green that you couldn't see the bottom. Plus, weeds grew thick around the far end of the lake. "Stay away from that end of the lake," my mom always said. "Those weeds are so thick you could drown."

My older brother Jimmy told me a swamp monster lived in those weeds that would come out from the lake at night to hunt little boys. I'd pull my covers over my head and worry that my screen was not solid enough to hold the swamp monster back. Some nights when I got the courage, I'd leap out of bed, run to the window,

and slam it shut. When I awakened in the morning, it would be open, and I would be alive. But it never stopped me from worrying that one night, Mom and Dad would find me gone with my screen ripped open. A trail of lake weeds would be the only thing left of me. I was just a little kid. I didn't know any better.

One night, just after my eighth birthday, I heard someone shouting.

"Help!" I heard.

Then, "Help!" again.

I pulled my covers over my head thinking it was the swamp monster, and he had finally gotten some unfortunate little boy. I thought of my friend Billy. I imagined him being pulled from his bed and dragged across his back lawn, kicking and screaming.

"Help!" I heard it again. It didn't sound like Billy. More like a girl. More like Mom. "Jim? Steven? Help!" It was Mom. The swamp monster had Mom.

In a burst of courage, I leaped from my bed and ran down the stairs. I rushed to the back door shouting, "I'll save you! I'll save you!" I quickly unlocked the door and bounded headfirst into Mom, knocking her over.

"Mom," I said, "What are you doing here? I thought—" but I caught myself before I spilled out, "I thought the swamp monster had you."

"I forgot my keys, and Jim locked the door when he went to bed," she said as she picked herself up from the porch. "I just went to the Watsons to help Mrs. Watson hem a dress. Did I frighten you?"

"N-no," I stuttered. "I just thought you were hurt. I'm glad you're okay, Mom," I said with a smile. As I looked out into the dark, I thought about the swamp monster. It didn't seem so scary any more. You never knew when one thing might turn out to be something else—something much less scary!

GO

1. **What is the setting of the story?**

_____

_____

_____

2. **Who tells the story? How old is the narrator?**

_____

_____

_____

3. **Which of the following adjectives best describe the narrator?**
   - (A) calm and rational
   - (B) brave and unconcerned
   - (C) fearful and excitable
   - (D) relaxed and unimaginative

4. **What is the conflict in the story?**

_____

_____

_____

_____

_____

5. **Why does the narrator tell us this story?**

_____

_____

_____

_____

_____

_____

6. **Does the narrator still believe in swamp monsters? How do you know?**

_____

_____

_____

_____

_____

7. **Some stories do not have a theme about people or life, but all stories have a purpose: to inform, entertain, expose, or illustrate. What is the purpose of this story?**

_____

_____

_____

_____

STOP

**English/
Language Arts**

ELA5R1

Identifying
Dramatic Structures

DIRECTIONS: Read the passage and then answer the questions.

Act 1, Scene 1

A sunny, bright spring day. Kaye and her friend Tasha are walking in the woods. As they walked, they noticed many squirrels running in the same direction.

Tasha: Let's follow them to see where they are going!

Kaye: *(with excitement)* Great idea!

Girls exit stage and the lights dim.

Act 1, Scene 2

A large clearing in the forest. The squirrels dashing about pause when the girls enter.

Squirrel: *(to girls)* Would you care to join us for lunch? We are having nuts!

Tasha and Kaye look at each other, then exclaim together: Sure!

---

1. This passage is which genre (type) of literature?

- (A) poetry
- (B) short story
- (C) drama
- (D) none of these

2. How many acts are in this passage?

- (F) one
- (G) two
- (H) three
- (J) none

3. How many scenes are in this passage?

- (A) one
- (B) two
- (C) three
- (D) none

4. The purpose of this genre is usually to _____ .

- (F) entertain the reader
- (G) alarm the reader
- (H) inform the reader
- (J) challenge the reader

5. This genre usually includes _____ .

- (A) accurate information
- (B) cartoon characters
- (C) stage direction
- (D) words that rhyme

6. The cast of characters for this passage would include _____ .

- (F) Tasha and Kaye
- (G) Tasha and the squirrels
- (H) Kaye and the squirrels
- (J) Tasha, Kaye, and the squirrels

STOP

Georgia Test Practice

ELA5R1

Identifying Personification

DIRECTIONS: Read the passage and then answer the questions.

Autumn Dance

Every October, autumn bullies summer into letting go of the skies. The wind breathes a chill into the air. The sun gets tired and goes to bed earlier each night, and night sleeps in later each day. The trees dress in bright gowns for the last celebration of the season, and the leaves are skipping and dancing down the sidewalk. This is autumn, standing firm with hands on her hips, until winter peers over the edge of the world.

1. This passage tells about _____ .

- (A) winter turning into spring
- (B) fall turning into winter
- (C) spring turning into summer
- (D) summer turning into fall

2. How does the sun change during autumn?

- (F) It rises and sets earlier than in the summer.
- (G) It rises and sets later than in the summer.
- (H) It rises later but sets earlier than in the summer.
- (J) It rises earlier but sets later than in the summer.

3. What is the author referring to when she describes the trees dressed in "bright gowns"?

- (A) leaves that have changed color but have not yet fallen from the trees
- (B) green leaves
- (C) formal dresses
- (D) the trees' empty branches

4. Personification means giving human qualities to animals or objects. Which sentence is not an example of personification?

- (F) Every October, autumn bullies summer into letting go of the skies.
- (G) A cold wind blows.
- (H) The leaves skipped and danced down the sidewalk.
- (J) The sun gets tired and goes to bed.

STOP

**English/
Language Arts**

ELA5R1

Identifying Similes, Metaphors, and Alliteration

DIRECTIONS: Read the passage and answer the questions on the next page.

Sollie, the Rock

I've lived on a lake for most of my life. I've had lots of time to learn all sorts of fun things to do in the water. I think my favorite thing of all is water skiing. That's why I decided to invite my best friend, Sollie, over to give it a try.

Sollie had never been on skis before, but I knew Dad could help him learn, just like he helped me.

Water skiing is like flying. If you aren't afraid of getting up, you'll enjoy the ride. That's what I told Sollie before we spent the afternoon trying to get him up on skis for the first time.

I thought it would be easy. Sollie is a seal, sleek and smooth in the water, bobbing in and out of the waves. I thought someone so agile would find skiing easy. It didn't dawn on me until the fourth try that Sollie is shaped more like a rock than a bird.

On his first try, Sollie let go of the towrope when Dad hit the gas. He sank as fast as the *Titanic.* The only things visible were the tips of his skis.

On his second try, Sollie leaned into the skis, flipping head over heels like a gymnast falling off the balance beam. His skis formed an "X" that marked the spot where he disappeared.

On the third try, Sollie stood up. He teetered forward and then back, as if he were a rag doll. His biggest mistake was holding on to the rope after he lost both skis. He flopped about behind the boat like a giant carp until he finally let go.

On the fourth try, Sollie bent his knees, straightened his back, and flew around the lake behind the boat as if he were a professional skier. He jumped the wake, rolled out next to the boat, and waved at me. He was "the man."

After three times around the lake, Sollie let go of the rope. He returned to his former self and dropped into the water like a rock.

After spending the afternoon out on the water with me and Dad, Sollie fell in love with water skiing. We made plans to do it again soon. Maybe even a rock can learn to fly!

GO

Georgia Test Practice

Metaphor—a direct comparison between unlike things. Example: Bobby is a mouse.

Simile—an indirect comparison between two unlike things using the words *like, as,* or *as if* to make the comparison. Example: Bobby is like a mouse.

Alliteration—the use of words that repeat the same beginning sound. Example: Round and round the rugged rock the ragged rascal ran.

1. **Identify the following lines as metaphors (M) or similes (S).**

    _____ Sollie is a seal, sleek and smooth in the water, bobbing in and out of the waves.

    _____ Sollie is shaped more like a rock than a bird.

    _____ He sank as fast as the *Titanic.*

    _____ He flopped about behind the boat like a giant carp until he finally let go.

2. **What do the above similes suggest about Sollie?**

    _____

    _____

    _____

    _____

    _____

    _____

3. **Why is the following sentence *not* a simile or a metaphor?**

    Sollie bent his knees, straightened his back, and flew around the lake behind the boat as if he were a professional skier.

    (A) It does not make a comparison.

    (B) It makes a comparison between like things.

    (C) It makes a contrast rather than a comparison.

    (D) The comparison is not between a person and an animal.

4. **Fill in the blank to turn the sentence into a simile.**

    Sollie bent his knees, straightened his back, and flew around the lake behind the boat . . .

    _____

    _____

    _____ .

5. **Identify the use of alliteration given in the fourth paragraph of the story.**

    _____

    _____

    _____

    _____

    _____

    _____

STOP

Identifying
Dialogue and Description

DIRECTIONS: This story is full of descriptive language whose sounds make you think of what they mean, such as *zooming* and *fizzing*. Words like these are examples of **onomatopoeia**. Read the story and use the clues to write the correct word from the story on the line. Each word will be an example of onomatopoeia.

Summer Storm

Brian went zooming to the park on his bike. It started out as a perfect day, until Brian's mom made him drag his little brother Pete along.

"Wait for me, Brian," whined Pete as he tried to keep up.

Brian parked his bike and followed his nose to the concession stand. There were sizzling burgers on the grill, freshly-popped popcorn, and big barrels of fizzing root beer. He made his purchase and handed Pete his lunch. "Sit here and eat, and don't move until I come back to get you," Brian said.

As Pete began eating, he heard the pitter-patter of rain falling around him, but he stayed dry under the large tree. As the rain increased, the wind began to howl. With the leaves rustling above his head, it sounded as though it was raining harder. Then he heard the plink of the hail on the metal roof of the concession stand. When Pete saw lightning in the distance, he knew he should move from under the tree. Brian would just have to look for him.

When the storm got worse, Brian knew he had to find Pete. Brian thought he heard his name as he ran, but then wondered if it was the wind playing tricks on him. There it was again. "Brian!" That voice had never sounded so good.

1. **moving rapidly**

_____

_____

2. **sharp metallic sound**

_____

_____

3. **soft crackling sound**

_____

_____

4. **sound of soft drops**

DIRECTIONS: Answer the following questions.

5. **What is the setting of this story?**

_____

_____

6. **Give two examples of dialogue from the story.**

_____

_____

_____

7. **Give one example of a vivid description from the story.**

_____

_____

STOP

Name _____ Date _____

ELA5R1

Analyzing Poetic Elements

DIRECTIONS: Modern poets often write **free-verse poems.** As the term indicates, the poet is free from conventions; free-verse poems do not contain regular rhythm or rhyme. Although poets may take certain liberties with the language, they often use natural rhythms and figures of speech, which help free-verse poems maintain their form. Answer the following questions about the poem.

Whitesox

Sanding the board,
My cat, Whitesox.
Her tongue,
Like fine grains of sand
On paper,
Licking the wood.
An electric sander
Giving out a quiet purr.
Like a nail file,
Smoothing out the edges.

Ouch! A splinter.

1. To what does the poet compare the cat's tongue?

   _____
   _____

2. What two things in the poem could be "giving out a quiet purr"?

   _____
   _____

3. Circle the periods in the poem. Does every line end with a period? What can you conclude about free-verse poems after seeing where the poet ends sentences?

   _____
   _____

4. What might the "splinter" be that Whitesox comes across in the process of cleaning himself?

   _____
   _____

5. Write a free-verse poem of your own about a pet.

   _____
   _____
   _____
   _____
   _____
   _____
   _____

STOP

Name _____ Date _____

Identifying Rhyme Scheme in Poetry

DIRECTIONS: Poets who set up a pattern of rhymes at the end of each line are creating a rhyme scheme. In a **rhyme scheme**, the first line is designated **a**, and all lines that rhyme with that word are also designated **a**. If the next line does not rhyme with the first, it is designated **b**.

Example:

Each day I walk to school and see	(a)
A lot of people driving cars.	(b)
Why don't they choose to walk, like me?	(a)

By the Ocean
As she walked along the sandy shore
With delight as nature's wonders she did see
Starfish, whitecaps, conch shells, and more.
She knew that she would never fly free
Like the tissue-paper seagulls above
Or swim with the dolphins she did love.

1. At the end of each line, label the "By the Ocean" poem with the correct rhyme scheme. Then fill in the following chart, placing words that rhyme together.

a	b	c

2. Make a list of your own rhyming words about the ocean. Use them as a starting point for writing a poem.

_____

_____

_____

**English/
Language Arts**

ELA5R1

Identifying Hyperbole

DIRECTIONS: Read the poem and answer the questions about **hyperbole.** Then write your own hyperbole.

 Clue   **Hyperbole** is using exaggeration to expess strong emotions.

My Backpack

My backpack's so heavy
It must weigh a ton.
With thousands of books—
My work's never done.

My arms are so sore
I can't lift a pen.
My breath is so short
I need oxygen.

When I stoop over,
It makes me fall down.
I think I'll just stay here
All squashed on the ground.

---

1. **Which of the following phrases is an example of hyperbole?**

   Ⓐ It makes me fall down.

   Ⓑ My work's never done.

   Ⓒ My breath is so short.

   Ⓓ It must weigh a ton.

2. **The poet decided there were too many exaggerations in the poem. Which of the following revised lines still contains a hyperbole?**

   Ⓕ My backpack is so heavy, it's hard to lift.

   Ⓖ My arms are so sore, I can't lift a pen.

   Ⓗ With four small textbooks, my work's almost done.

   Ⓙ My breath is so short, I need to rest.

3. **Write your own hyperboles. Remember that you should include exaggeration as part of your description.**

   My dog is so ugly,

   _____

   _____ .

   I am so tired,

   _____

   _____ .

STOP

**English/
Language Arts**

ELA5R1

Comparing Characters and Themes

DIRECTIONS: Read the stories and then answer the questions.

Walks All Over the Sky

Back when the sky was completely dark, there was a chief with two sons—a younger son, One Who Walks All Over the Sky, and an older son, Walking About Early. The younger son was sad to see the sky always so dark so he made a mask out of wood and pitch (the sun) and lit it on fire. Each day, he travels across the sky. At night, he sleeps below the horizon, and when he snores sparks fly from the mask and make the stars. The older brother became jealous. To impress their father, he smeared fat and charcoal on his face (the moon) and makes his own path across the sky.

—From the *Tsimshian of the Pacific Northwest*

The Porcupine

Once, Porcupine and Beaver argued about the seasons. Porcupine wanted five winter months. He held up one hand and showed his five fingers. He said, "Let the winter months be the same in number as the fingers on my hand." Beaver said, "No," and held up his tail, which had many cracks or scratches on it. He said, "Let the winter months be the same in number as the scratches on my tail." They argued more and Porcupine got angry and bit off his thumb. Then, holding up his hand with the four fingers, he said, "There must be only four winter months." Beaver was afraid and gave in. For this reason, today porcupines have four claws on each foot.

—From the *Tahltan: Teit, Journal of American Folk-Lore, xxxii, 226*

These stories are from different cultures, but their themes are similar. Both try to explain something.

1. What is explained in the first story?

_____

_____

2. What is explained in the second story?

_____

_____

3. Who are the two characters in the first story? In the second story?

_____

_____

4. How is the relationship between the characters in the first story and the characters in the second story alike?

_____

_____

_____

STOP

Name _____   Date _____

Identifying
Literary Structures

DIRECTIONS: The heroine of this poem was Mary Redmond, and she lived in Philadelphia. During the occupation of that town by the British, she was always ready to aid in the secret delivery of the letters written home by the husbands and fathers fighting in the Continental Army. After reading the poem below, complete each portion of the story map on the next page.

Black-Eyed Rebel
A poem by Will Carleton

A boy drove into the city, his wagon loaded down
With food to feed the people of the British-governed town;
And the little black-eyed rebel, so innocent and sly,
Was watching for his coming from the corner of her eye. . .

He drove up to the market, he waited in the line;
His apples and potatoes were fresh and fair and fine;
But long and long he waited, and no one came to buy,
Save the black-eyed rebel, watching from the corner of her eye.

"Now who will buy my apples?" he shouted, long and loud;
And "Who wants my potatoes?" he repeated to the crowd;
But from all the people 'round him came no word of reply,
Save the black-eyed rebel, answering from the corner of her eye.

For she knew that 'neath the lining of the coat he wore that day,
Were long letters from the husbands and the fathers far away,
Who were fighting for the freedom that they meant to gain or die;
And a tear like silver glistened in the corner of her eye.

But the treasures—how to get them? crept the questions through her mind,
Since keen enemies were watching for what prizes they might find:
And she paused a while and pondered, with a pretty little sigh;
Then resolve crept through her features, and a shrewdness fired her eye.

So she resolutely walked up to the wagon old and red;
"May I have a dozen apples for a kiss?" she sweetly said:
And the brown face flushed to scarlet; for the boy was somewhat shy,
And he saw her laughing at him from the corner of her eye. . .

Clinging round his brawny neck, she clasped her fingers white and small,
And then whispered, "Quick! the letters! thrust them underneath my shawl!
Carry back again this package, and be sure that you are spry!"
And she sweetly smiled upon him from the corner of her eye. . .

With the news of loved ones absent to the dear friends they would greet,
Searching them who hungered for them, swift she glided through the street.
"There is nothing worth the doing that it does not pay to try,"
Thought the little black-eyed rebel, with a twinkle in her eye.

GO

Setting

1. _____
_____

Main Characters

2. _____
_____

Plot

3. _____
_____
_____
_____

Episodes

4. _____
_____
_____
_____

Climax

5. _____
_____
_____
_____
_____

Resolution

6. _____
_____
_____
_____

Refrain

7. **A refrain is a phrase that is repeated throughout a text. What words or phrases are repeated in this poem?**

_____
_____

STOP

English/
Language Arts

ELA5R1

Locating Facts in Texts

DIRECTIONS: Read the passage and then answer the questions on the next page.

The Panama Canal

When the Panama Canal was completed in 1914, it became one of the greatest engineering wonders in the world. Built by the United States, the canal is a waterway that cuts across the Isthmus of Panama. It links the Atlantic Ocean and the Pacific Ocean. Prior to the opening of the Panama Canal, ships traveling from one ocean to the other had to sail around South America. With the canal, ships sailed approximately 6,000 miles traveling from New York to San Francisco. Before the canal opened, ships sailed more than 15,000 miles to make the same voyage.

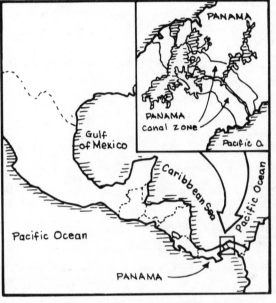

For hundreds of years, people knew the importance of a waterway across Central America. In 1903, the United States signed a treaty with Panama, which allowed the United States to build and operate a canal.

One of the first obstacles to overcome in building the canal was disease, which plagued the Isthmus of Panama. Special medical teams went to the area to improve sanitary conditions. Efforts were made to rid the area of mosquitoes, which carried malaria and yellow fever.

In 1906, it was decided that the canal would be built as a series of locks. The locks would be cheaper and quicker to build. In 1907, an army engineer named Colonel George Goethals was put in charge of the project. Construction began with three main tasks: excavate earth to clear passages, build a dam across the Chagres River, and build the series of locks. Thousands of workers used steam shovels and dredges to cut passages through hills, swamps, and jungles.

The completed canal cost $380 million. It runs 50 miles across the Isthmus of Panama from Limon Bay in the Atlantic to the Bay of Panama in the Pacific. The water in the canal is controlled by three sets of locks, or water-filled chambers. Each lock is 110 feet wide and 70 feet deep. All but the very largest of today's ships can pass through the canal.

In 1977, the Panama Canal Treaty was signed. In this treaty, the United States transferred the responsibility for administration, upkeep, and maintenance of the canal to the Republic of Panama. On December 31, 1999, the transfer of authority was completed.

GO

Name _____ Date _____

DIRECTIONS: Fill in the correct answers to complete the summary paragraph below.

The Panama Canal was completed in

(1) _____ .

It became one of the greatest engineering wonders in

the world. The canal was built by

(2) _____

and cuts across the

(3) _____ of **(4)** _____ .

The Panama Canal links the

(5) _____ Ocean

and the **(6)** _____ Ocean.

DIRECTIONS: Complete the statements below.

7. **The main reason for building the canal was**

_____

_____ .

8. **One of the first major obstacles to overcome in building the canal was**

_____ .

Construction of the canal began with three major tasks:

9. _____

10. _____

11. _____

Three facts about the completed canal:

12. _____

13. _____

14. _____

Summarize the role of each country with the canal.

15. **The Republic of Panama**

_____

_____

_____

16. **The United States**

_____

_____

_____

_____

Summarize the two major treaties between the United States and the Republic of Panama.

17. 1903 _____

_____

_____

18. 1977 _____

_____

_____

STOP

English/
Language Arts

ELA5R1

Paragraphs and Topic Sentences

DIRECTIONS: Read each paragraph. Choose the answer that fills in the blank as the best topic sentence for the paragraph.

Clue — A paragraph should be about one idea. All the sentences should relate to that idea.

1. _____ A honeybee collects pollen and nectar from a flower. When the bee goes to the next flower, some of the pollen from the first flower falls onto the second. The second flower uses this pollen to make seeds.

   (A) It is estimated that honeybees pollinate billions of dollars worth of crops each year.

   (B) The most important role of the honeybee is to pollinate plants.

   (C) If you are stung by a bee, remove the stinger carefully.

   (D) Bees are considered pests.

2. _____ Toads and tree frogs croak in the evenings. Sometimes the chirping of the crickets is so loud that you can't hear the little frogs. But the booming of the big bullfrogs can always be heard. I don't know how Lane Roy sleeps.

   (F) Crickets are louder than frogs.

   (G) Swamps are homes to many different creatures.

   (H) Frogs make a variety of sounds.

   (J) The swamp behind the house is filled with sound.

3. _____ Snails produce a liquid on the bottom of their feet. Then they "surf" on the rippling waves of this sticky liquid. Sea stars have slender tube feet with tiny suction cups that help them grip. Dolphins whip their tails up and down to thrust their bodies through the water.

   (A) Animals eat a variety of foods found in nature.

   (B) There are many different animals in the United States.

   (C) Animals move about in many unusual ways.

   (D) Animals have different kinds of feet.

4. _____ In her diary, Anne found comfort. She described her cramped living conditions, the families' quarrels and difficulties, and her fears and joys. After her father returned from the war, he was given Anne's diary. Since then, it's been published in more than 55 languages.

   (F) Her father, Otto, was a businessman.

   (G) For two years, Anne lived in a secret annex.

   (H) When Otto was released from the concentration camp, he returned to Amsterdam.

   (J) During her hiding period, Anne Frank kept a diary.

**English/
Language Arts**

Reading

ELA5R1

Using Graphics to Enhance Meaning

DIRECTIONS: Read the passage and answer the questions below.

Easter Island

Few places in the world are more intriguing and mystifying than Easter Island, located in the Pacific Ocean, 2,300 miles from the coast of Chile. Easter Island has 64 square miles of rugged coastline and steep hills. Scientists believe the island began as a volcano. Three extinct volcanoes remain on the island. The largest one rises 1,400 feet high.

On Easter Sunday in 1722, Dutch Admiral Jacob Roggeveen and his crew landed on Easter Island aboard the Dutch ship *Arena.* The astonished crew found dozens of huge stone figures standing on long stone platforms. The statues, some measuring 40 feet tall, were similar in appearance. Their expressionless faces were without eyes. Huge red stone cylinders were placed on their heads. Since that time, the island has been a source of mystery and intrigue to scientists and explorers.

Scientists believe that the statues were carved from hard volcanic rock in the crater walls of the volcano called *Rana Raraku.* The statues were chiseled with stone picks made of basalt. Although the statues weigh many tons each, it is believed that they were moved with ropes and rollers across the island and placed on long platforms. This may be the reason for one island legend about the statues "walking" to their site.

Today, Easter Island is governed by Chile, a country of South America. Almost the entire population of 2,000 people live in the small village of Hanga Roa on the west coast of the island.

1. **Which of the following best describes the graphics that accompany this passage?**

   Ⓐ a chart and a map

   Ⓑ a diagram and a map

   Ⓒ a map and an illustration

   Ⓓ a chart and an illustration

2. **Name two ways in which the meaning of the passage is enhanced by the accompanying graphics.**

   _____

   _____

   _____

   STOP

24

English/
Language Arts   **Reading**

ELA5R1

Using Chronological Order

DIRECTIONS: Read the passage and then answer the questions on the next page.

The Hot-Air Balloon

For thousands of years, people have been fascinated with the idea of flying. The idea was especially appealing to two French brothers, Jacques and Joseph Montgolfier. In the late 1700s, they began experimenting with the idea of a hot-air balloon.

Their first experiment was to fill small paper bags with smoke. They found that the bags would rise in the air. The Montgolfiers first believed that the smoke made the bags rise. But later, they realized it was the hot air, and not the smoke itself, that caused the bags to rise.

The Montgolfier brothers continued to experiment. In 1783, they put a hot-air balloon in the air for eight minutes. The balloon carried a rooster, a sheep, and a duck! They landed safely after history's first real balloon flight.

Later that year, French scientist Jean de Rozier and French nobleman Marquis d'Arlandes became the first people to make a free flight in a hot-air balloon. The balloon was made by the Montgolfier brothers. It rose over 300 feet into the air. The flight lasted 25 minutes as de Rozier floated over Paris, France.

About the same time that the Montgolfier brothers were making their hot-air balloons, another Frenchman, named Jacques Charles, was making a balloon that was filled with hydrogen, a gas that is lighter than air. In December of 1783, Charles made the first flight in a hydrogen balloon. His balloon rose over 2,000 feet into the air. He flew 25 miles from where he started.

In 1784, ballooning became very popular in France. People traveled for miles to see balloons take off and land. Many of the balloonists became heroes. On January 7, 1785, two men made the first balloon flight across the English Channel. The flight from England to France took two hours.

Through the years, balloons have been used for sport. But since their invention, balloons have been used for more serious purposes, too. In the 1700s and 1800s, balloons were used in wars to observe the enemy troops. In 1863, an American balloonist named Thaddeus Lowe directed a balloon corps that flew for the Union Army. Balloons were also used in World War I and World War II.

Today, hot-air balloons are made of nylon or polyester. To fly a balloon, the pilot burns fuel to produce hot air, which inflates the balloon. The balloon rises into the air as more hot air is produced. To lower the balloon, hot air is released.

GO ➡

Name _____ Date _____

DIRECTIONS: Fill in the time line below with five important events in the history of hot-air ballooning from 1783 to 1863. Answer the following questions based on the passage.

1.

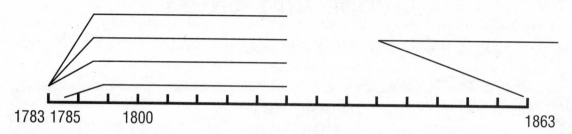

1783 1785   1800   1863

2. **The main purpose of the article is _____ .**

   (A) to examine the contributions of the Montgolfier brothers

   (B) to explore the differences between hot-air balloons and hydrogen balloons

   (C) to review the early history of hot-air ballooning in France

   (D) to compare hot-air balloons of the past and present

3. **Through the years, balloons have been used _____ .**

   (F) to carry animals

   (G) to observe enemy troops

   (H) for sport

   (J) all of the above

4. **Which of the following puts the hot-air balloon creations of the Montgolfier brothers in the correct order?**

   (A) smoke-filled bags, hot-air balloon carrying animals, hot-air balloon carrying a person

   (B) hot-air balloon carrying animals, hot air balloon carrying a person, hydrogen balloon

   (C) smoke-filled bags, hot-air balloon carrying a person, hydrogen balloon

   (D) hydrogen balloon, smoke-filled bags, hot-air balloon carrying people

DIRECTIONS: Write a **T** if the statement is true and an **F** if the statement is false.

5. _____ **In 1783, the Montgolfier brothers put a hot-air balloon in the air.**

6. _____ **Smoke made hot-air balloons rise.**

7. _____ **One of the first balloons carried a dog, mule, and duck.**

8. _____ **Jean de Rozier was one of the first people to ride in a hot-air balloon.**

9. _____ **His flight lasted 25 minutes as he floated over Paris.**

10. _____ **The Montgolfiers' balloons were filled with hydrogen.**

STOP

Georgia Test Practice

English/
Language Arts

ELA5R1

Distinguishing
Cause and Effect

DIRECTIONS: Read the passage and then complete the chart on the next page.

✦ Television

The invention of the television changed the world in many important ways. Television has given people the opportunity to see and hear people, places, and events from around the world. Over 98 percent of all U.S. homes have a television. Television is now an important form of communication, allowing people instant access to current events.

Television does not have just one inventor. In the 1800s, an Italian inventor named Marconi discovered how to send signals through the air as electromagnetic waves. His invention was the radio. This set the stage for the invention of television. In the early 1900s, a young American named Philo Farnsworth began experimenting. He had an idea to send pictures as well as sound through the air. This idea resulted in the invention of the electronic television camera.

About the same time, an American scientist named Vladimir Zworykin invented the iconoscope and the kinescope. The iconoscope was a television camera. The kinescope was a picture tube to receive and show the picture. In 1929, Zworykin made the first television system.

But how does a television work? The picture that you see is the result of three steps. First, light and sound waves are changed into electronic signals. The light and sound waves come from the scene that is being televised. Next, these electronic signals are passed through the air to be received by individual television sets. Last, the television set unscrambles the signals. In this way, a picture is "moved" from the original scene to your television set.

These three steps happen because light and sound waves can be made into electronic signals. Light waves are picked up and changed into electronic signals by a camera. Sound waves are picked up and changed into electronic signals by a microphone. The camera signals are called *video,* and the microphone signals are called *audio.*

To produce electric signals in color, certain color signals are added to the video. Three primary colors of light—red, blue, and green—are used to produce pictures in color.

With the advent of digital technology, televisions have wider screens and pictures that are even clearer.

GO

Cause	Effect
1.	Television pictures appear in color.
A camera picks up light waves.	2.
Vladimir Zworykin invents the iconoscope and the kinescope.	3.
4.	The electronic television camera is invented.
5.	People can see and hear people, places, and events from around the world.
Over 98 percent of all U.S. homes have a television.	6.
7.	Electronic signals are received by television sets.
Marconi invents the radio.	8.
9.	A picture is "moved" from the original scene to a television set.
Digital technology is becoming readily available.	10.

STOP

Georgia Test Practice

Identifying Main Ideas

(1) Imagine a 17-year-old girl going to her king and telling him she would like to lead his army to victory. Even more amazing, imagine the king agreeing with her. You may think this is a far-fetched story, but it really happened.

(2) The year was 1429. Joan of Arc was only 17 years old when she went to King Charles VII of France to tell him she had seen a vision and heard the voices of saints. God wanted her to free France from the English. She was to lead the French army in battle against the English at Orleans.

(3) The king wanted to test her to see if she really did possess extraordinary powers. He disguised himself and put one of his noblemen on the throne. Joan saw right through the disguise and went immediately to the real king with her request. He tested her again, and she was able to tell him what he prayed to God when he was alone. The king was convinced of her powers.

(4) Joan and her army went to Orleans in April of 1429 and defeated the English in only ten days. Charles had never been officially crowned king because the city of Reims, the coronation site for French kings, was in enemy territory. After the victory at Orleans, Joan escorted Charles to Reims, where he was crowned King on July 17, 1429.

(5) Joan wanted to free France completely from the English, so she went again into battle outside Paris. This time she was wounded and captured by the English. Rather than return her to the French in exchange for a ransom, as was the custom, the English kept her as a prisoner.

(6) Like the French, the English also believed Joan had supernatural powers. Where the French king thought they came from God, the English thought they were from the devil. Joan was charged with witchcraft by a French tribunal sympathetic to the English. She was found guilty and burned at the stake on May 30, 1431, in Rouen, France. Her ashes were thrown into the Seine River.

(7) Later, her family requested a new trial, and in 1456, she was found innocent. Although it was too late to save her life, she was declared a saint. Saint Joan of Arc is recognized on the date of her death, May 30.

GO

Name _____ Date _____

DIRECTIONS: Read the passage on the previous page and then choose the main idea of each numbered paragraph.

1. (A) Something amazing might happen involving a 17-year-old girl and a king.

   (B) This story is not possible; therefore, it is fiction.

   (C) A king does not allow a 17-year-old girl to join the army.

   (D) A story about a girl asking her king if she may lead his army is really true.

2. (F) Joan did not tell the king about her vision.

   (G) Joan of Arc led the French army in a battle at Orleans.

   (H) Joan was 17 when she went to see the king.

   (J) Joan heard voices telling her to lead the French in battle.

3. (A) Joan was a good test-taker.

   (B) The king tested Joan to see if what she claimed was true.

   (C) She did not pass the first test, so she had to take another.

   (D) Joan refused to be tested.

4. (F) Joan was a military genius who defeated the English.

   (G) The king was not officially crowned because the English held Reims.

   (H) After defeating the English, Joan led the king to Reims to be officially crowned.

   (J) Since Joan could not defeat the English, the king was not crowned.

5. (A) Joan liked wars, so she kept fighting until her capture by the English.

   (B) Joan was wounded, and the French army wanted to stop fighting.

   (C) In a battle near Paris, Joan was wounded, captured, and held prisoner by the English.

   (D) The French army would not pay a ransom to the English to get Joan back.

6. (F) Joan was found to have no supernatural powers.

   (G) Joan was tried for witchcraft and burned at the stake.

   (H) There is a debate about whether Joan's power came from God or the devil.

   (J) Joan's ashes were thrown into the Seine River.

7. (A) Joan's family wanted to bring her back to life, so they requested a new trial.

   (B) Joan was later found innocent and declared to be a saint.

   (C) Joan is recognized on the date of her death.

   (D) Joan's family requested a new trial, and she was found guilty again.

STOP

Name _____   Date _____

Relating New Information to Prior Knowledge

DIRECTIONS: Before reading the passage below, examine the following information:

- Ancient Greece existed over 2,000 years ago.

- The ancient Greeks developed democracy, a way of life that allowed the people to take part in their own government.

- The people of ancient Greece worshipped many different gods. Each year they celebrated festivals in honor of their gods. The most famous festival was called the Olympic Games.

- The people of ancient Greece ate only two meals a day.

- The men and women of ancient Greece wore cloaks and sandals.

Now read the passage and answer the questions based on your knowledge of ancient Greece.

Ancient Rome was a powerful civilization that began almost 3,000 years ago. The ancient Romans were very interested in law and government. One principle they established that is still in use today is called *equity.* It means that a law should be flexible enough to fit different circumstances.

Dinner was the largest of the three meals eaten each day, often served as a banquet. Clothing was simple and comfortable, and both men and women wore a short-sleeved garment called a *tunica.* Men wore a draped cloth, called a *toga,* over the tunica.

The Romans worshipped many gods. The Romans later adopted some of the Greek gods and goddesses and gave them new names. For example, the Greek goddess Aphrodite became the Roman goddess Venus.

The ancient Romans were famous for their many festivals, which were usually held in the huge open theater called the *Colosseum.* The Colosseum is still standing today. One of the most popular events was the chariot race, which was held in a large arena called a *circus.* The largest circus in ancient Rome was the Circus Maximus, which held 180,000 Roman spectators.

1. **Which society existed first—ancient Greece or ancient Rome?** _____

2. **True or false: Romans developed the concept of democracy.** _____

3. **True or false: The Olympic Games originated in ancient Rome.** _____

4. **Based on the reading, which of the following is an accurate judgment?**

   Ⓐ The people in both societies were concerned about how they dressed.

   Ⓑ Neither society cared much about festivals.

   Ⓒ Worshipping many different gods was important to the people in both societies.

   Ⓓ The people in both societies liked to eat a lot.

**English/
Language Arts**

ELA5R1

For pages 8–31

Mini-Test 1

Reading

DIRECTIONS: Choose the best answer.

1. Act IV

Timothy enters his apartment and finds the furniture overturned and things thrown from the drawers. He picks up the telephone and dials 9-1-1.

TIMOTHY: *(fearfully)* Yes, I need to report a break-in! *(pause)* No, I haven't searched the entire apartment. *(pause)* Do you really think they could still be here?!

- (A) novel
- (B) play
- (C) poem
- (D) fable

**2. The children awoke to a happy sight.
While they slept, the world had turned white.
Their mother peered into their room and said,
"No school today. Go back to bed!"**

- (F) novel
- (G) play
- (H) poem
- (J) fable

3. What rhyme scheme is used in number 2?

- (A) aabb
- (B) abab
- (C) aabc
- (D) abba

4. I'm so hungry, I could eat a horse.

- (F) personification
- (G) hyperbole
- (H) simile
- (J) metaphor

5. Her hair was as black as coal.

- (A) personification
- (B) hyperbole
- (C) simile
- (D) metaphor

6. The skies cried great drops of tears.

- (F) personification
- (G) hyperbole
- (H) simile
- (J) metaphor

DIRECTIONS: Read the passage below and then answer the questions.

When we first climbed into the car and strapped on our safety belts, I wasn't very nervous. As we started to climb the hill, however, I could feel my heart jump into my throat. "Brian?" I asked my brother nervously. "Is this supposed to be so noisy?" "Sure, Matthew," Brian answered. "It always does that." A minute later, we whooshed so fast down the hill I didn't have time to think. With a twist, a loop, and a bunch of fast turns, everyone on board screamed in delight. By the time the car pulled into the station and we got off the ride, I was ready to do it again!

7. Which of the following best describes the setting of the story?

- (A) a car ride to school
- (B) a train ride
- (C) a ride on a roller coaster
- (D) a trip to the grocery store

Georgia Test Practice

8. From the beginning to the end of this story, Matthew went from being _____ .

    (F) nervous to calm to scared

    (G) calm to nervous to bored

    (H) bored to excited to scared

    (J) calm to nervous to excited

DIRECTIONS: Read the passage below and then answer questions 9–11.

There lived in Virginia in the early 1600s a beautiful girl named Pocahontas. Her name meant *Playful One.* She was the daughter of Powhatan, the chief of some 30 Native American groups in Virginia.

Pocahontas is remembered for saving the life of Captain John Smith. Smith was the leader of the Jamestown colony founded by the English in 1607. In that same year, he was captured by the Native Americans and sentenced to death by Chief Powhatan. According to Smith's own account, he was ordered to lay his head on large stones in anticipation of being clubbed to death by several braves. At this point, Pocahontas is said to have knelt beside the Englishman and placed her head on his. Powhatan was apparently touched by this gesture, and he ordered that Smith be set free.

In 1613, Pocahontas was captured and held hostage by the English. During her year of captivity, she met and married John Rolfe, a Virginia tobacco planter. In 1616, she accompanied Rolfe to England, where she was presented at the royal court. Pocahontas died there of smallpox in 1617, shortly before her planned return to America. She was buried at Gravesend, England.

9. Which of the following is the topic sentence in the second paragraph?

    (A) Smith was the leader of the Jamestown colony founded by the English in 1607.

    (B) In that same year, he was captured by the Native Americans and sentenced to death by Chief Powhatan.

    (C) Pocahontas is remembered for saving the life of Captain John Smith.

    (D) Powhatan was apparently touched by this gesture, and he ordered that Smith be set free.

10. Complete the cause and effect chart below using information from the passage.

Cause	Effect
	Powhatan was touched by this gesture and ordered that Smith be set free.
Pocahontas was captured and held hostage by the English.	

11. Which of the events below is missing from this sequence of events?

Pocahontas saved the life of John Smith.

The English captured Pocahontas.

Pocahontas traveled to England.

    (F) Chief Powhatan died.

    (G) Pocahontas married John Rolfe.

    (H) Pocahontas got smallpox.

    (J) John Rolfe was killed.

12. Based on your reading throughout the year, what is your favorite genre? Why?

_____

_____

_____

_____

STOP

Reading Standards

Reading Standards ELA5R1 and ELA5R2 *(See pages 6–7.)*

ELA5R3. The student understands and acquires new vocabulary and uses it correctly in reading and writing. *(See pages 36–43.)* **The student:**

a. reads a variety of texts and incorporates new words into oral and written language.
b. determines the meaning of unfamiliar words using context clues (e.g., definition, example).
c. determines the meaning of unfamiliar words using knowledge of common roots, suffixes, and prefixes.
d. determines pronunciations, meanings, alternate word choices, and parts of speech of words using dictionaries and thesauruses.
e. identifies the meaning of common prefixes (e.g., un-, re-, dis-).
f. identifies the meaning of common idioms and figurative phrases.
g. identifies playful uses of language (e.g., puns, jokes, palindromes).
h. recognizes and uses words with multiple meanings (e.g., sentence, school, hard) and determines which meaning is intended from the context of the sentence.
i. identifies and applies the meaning of the terms *antonym, synonym,* and *homophone.*

What it means:

- **Antonyms** are words with opposite meanings. For example, *sad* is an antonym for *happy.*
- **Synonyms** are words with similar meanings. For example, *cheerful* is a synonym for *happy.*
- **Homophones** are two or more words pronounced alike but spelled differently. For example, *hair* and *hare* are homophones.

ELA5R4. The student reads aloud, accurately (in the range of 95 percent), familiar material in a variety of genres of the quality and complexity illustrated in the sample reading list, in a way that makes meaning clear to listeners. *(See page 43.)* **The student:**

a. uses letter-sound knowledge to decode written English and uses a range of cueing systems (e.g., phonics and context clues) to determine pronunciation and meaning.
b. uses self-correction when subsequent reading indicates an earlier miscue (self-monitoring and self-correcting strategies).
c. reads with a rhythm, flow, and meter that sounds like everyday speech (prosody).

Reading Standards

Grade Five Reading List

This is a sample reading list from which the students and teachers could select. This list is not exclusive. Acceptable titles also appear on lists produced by organizations such as the National Council of Teachers of English and the American Library Association. Substitutions might also be made from lists approved locally.

Fiction

Armstrong, *Sounder*
Avi, *Poppy*
Avi, *Something Upstairs*
Blume, *Here's to You, Rachel Robinson*
Burnett, *The Secret Garden*
Byars, *The Pinballs*
Dahl, *The BFG*
Farley, *The Black Stallion*
Fitzhugh, *Harriet the Spy*
Gantos, Joey Pigza series
Greer, *Max and Me and the Time Machine*
Kipling, *The Jungle Book*
Lewis, *The Lion, the Witch, and the Wardrobe*
Lincoln, *The Gettysburg Address*
Lord, *In the Year of the Boar and Jackie Robinson*
Lowry, *Number the Stars*
Paterson, *The Great Gilly Hopkins*
Paulsen, *Brian's Winter*
Paulsen, *Hatchet*
Paulsen, *Mr. Tucket*
Paulsen, *Nightjohn*
Paulsen, *Soldier's Heart*
Paulsen, *The Rifle*
Slote, *Finding Buck McHenry*
Wallace, *Never Say Quit*

Nonfiction

Conklin, *The Titanic Sinks*
Epstein, *Anne Frank*
Fritz, *Where Do You Think You're Going, Christopher Columbus?*
January, *The Dred Scott Decision (Cornerstone of Freedom)*
January, *The Emancipation Proclamation (Cornerstone of Freedom)*
Kent, *The Disability Rights Movement (Cornerstone of Freedom)*
Markham, *Lois Lowry*
Parks, *Rosa Parks: My Story*
Paulsen, *My Life in Dog Years*
Simon, *Earthquakes*
Spinelli, *Knots in My Yo-Yo String: The Autobiography of a Kid*
Sterling, *Freedom Train: The Story of Harriet Tubman*

Poetry

Thomas, *Brown Honey and Broomwheat Tea*

Using Context Clues to Determine Meaning

DIRECTIONS: Read the sentences below. Find the answer choice that best completes each number blank in the sentences.

The United States Capitol is well known for its **(1)** ___C___ , or circular room. The room is covered by a large dome, or round **(2)** ___F___ , with a bronze Statue of Freedom on top.

1.
- (A) parlor
- (B) library
- (C) rotunda
- (D) media center

2.
- (F) roof
- (G) floor
- (H) wall
- (J) door

DIRECTIONS: Read the poem and answer the questions that follow.

Bishop Loreless

"Bishop Loreless" is an English poem that was written more than 600 years ago. The English language has changed quite a bit since then. Even though this poem is written in English, you are probably not familiar with some of the words. Use the definitions that accompany the poem to help your understanding.

Bishop loreless,°
King redeless,°
Young men reckless,°
Old man witless
Woman shameless—
    I swear by heaven's king
    Those be five lither thing!

°lore—learning, knowledge
°redeless—without advice or guidance
°reckless—heedless

3. The best definition of the word *loreless* is _____ .
- (A) knowledgeable
- (B) irresponsible
- (C) ignorant
- (D) wicked

4. A definition for the phrase *lither thing* is not provided for you. Based on the rest of the poem, what do you think the phrase means?
- (F) respectable things
- (G) beautiful things
- (H) evil things
- (J) happy things

English/ Language Arts

ELA5R3

Using Roots to Determine Meaning

DIRECTIONS: Choose the best answer.

1. If *portare* means "to carry" in Latin, then which of these words probably means something that can be easily carried about?

   - (A) transport
   - (B) portable
   - (C) portion
   - (D) portrait

2. If *prae* means "in front of" or "before" in Latin, then which of these words probably means the introductory, or first part, of a constitution?

   - (F) predator
   - (G) preamble
   - (H) precious
   - (J) precede

3. If *tolerare* means "to bear pain" in Latin, then which of these words probably means to put up with?

   - (A) tool
   - (B) total
   - (C) tolerate
   - (D) torture

4. Which of these words probably comes from the Latin word *albus* meaning "white?"

   - (F) albino
   - (G) album
   - (H) algebra
   - (J) alchemy

DIRECTIONS: Choose the correct definition for the root in each word.

5. In the word *abbreviate*, brev means _____ .

   - (A) to lengthen
   - (B) to shorten
   - (C) to make a list
   - (D) to learn how to spell

6. In the word *autograph*, graph means _____ .

   - (F) to read
   - (G) to draw a picture
   - (H) to write
   - (J) to measure something

7. In the word *telescope*, tele means _____ .

   - (A) empty space
   - (B) far away
   - (C) close up
   - (D) temperature

8. In the word *geography*, geo means _____ .

   - (F) stars
   - (G) earth
   - (H) the human body
   - (J) insects

9. In the word *bicycle*, cycl means _____ .

   - (A) wheel
   - (B) handlebars
   - (C) spokes
   - (D) chain

STOP

Prefixes and Suffixes

DIRECTIONS: Choose the answer that means the same as the underlined parts of the words.

1. care**less** thought**less**
   - (A) less than one
   - (B) full of
   - ✓(C) without
   - (D) forward

2. **sub**way **sub**marine
   - ✓(F) under
   - (G) over
   - (H) apart
   - (J) backward

3. **pre**arrange **pre**destined
   - ✓(A) before
   - (B) after
   - (C) apart
   - (D) within

4. **un**happy **un**natural
   - (F) full of
   - (G) across
   - (H) false
   - ✓(J) not

5. **co**operate **co**worker
   - (A) opposite of
   - (B) one
   - ✓(C) together
   - (D) before

6. **mis**spell **mis**treat
   - ✓(F) wrong
   - (G) beside
   - (H) correct
   - (J) not

7. **over**eat **over**spend
   - (A) without
   - ✓(B) excessive
   - (C) into
   - (D) before

8. **de**frost **de**grease
   - (F) give up
   - (G) enter
   - ✓(H) remove
   - (J) half

DIRECTIONS: Fill in the blank with a word or phrase that explains the meaning of the underlined part of the word.

9. **Re**play means to play _again_.

10. A **dis**honest person is one who is _not_ honest.

11. Something that is treat**able** _can_ treated.

12. An invent**or** is _person_ invents.

13. Someone who is fool**ish** is _playing_ a fool.

14. A **post**game party is a party _____ the game.

STOP

Name _____   Date _____

Using Dictionaries and Thesauruses

DIRECTIONS: Use the dictionary entries to answer questions 1–3.

save [sāv] *v.* **1.** to rescue from harm or danger **2.** to keep in a safe condition **3.** to set aside for future use; store **4.** to avoid

saving [sā´vĭng] *n.* **1.** rescuing from harm or danger **2.** avoiding excess spending; economy **3.** something saved

savory [sā´və-rē] *adj.* **1.** appealing to the taste or smell **2.** salty to the taste

1. **The *a* in the word *saving* sounds most like the *a* in the word _____ .**

   Ⓐ pat

   Ⓑ ape

   Ⓒ heated

   Ⓓ naughty

2. **Which sentence uses *save* in the same way as definition number 3?**

   Ⓕ Firefighters save lives.

   Ⓖ She saves half of all she earns.

   Ⓗ Going by jet saves eight hours of driving.

   Ⓙ The life jacket saved the boy from drowning.

3. **Which sentence uses *savory* in the same way as definition number 2?**

   Ⓐ The savory stew made me thirsty.

   Ⓑ The savory bank opened an account.

   Ⓒ This flower has a savory scent.

   Ⓓ The savory dog rescued me.

DIRECTIONS: Use the sample thesaurus to answer questions 4–6. Choose the best synonym to replace the underlined word in each sentence.

> **head** [hed] *n.* **1.** skull, scalp, *noggin **2.** leader, commander, director, chief, manager **3.** top, summit, peak **4.** front **5.** toilet, restroom (on a boat)
>
> **head** [hed] *v.* **1.** lead, command, direct, supervise
>
> **Key:** *n.* noun, *v.* verb, *slang

4. **The brain is inside the <u>head</u>.**

   Ⓕ front

   Ⓖ top

   Ⓗ summit

   Ⓙ skull

5. **Captain Blaine was the <u>head</u> of the army.**

   Ⓐ commander

   Ⓑ top

   Ⓒ peak

   Ⓓ front

6. **How is the underlined word used in this sentence?**

   She was chosen to <u>head</u> the Art Club.

   Ⓕ noun

   Ⓖ adverb

   Ⓗ slang

   Ⓙ verb

English/
Language Arts

ELA5R3

Common Idioms

DIRECTIONS: Read the passage and then match each idiom with its meaning.

Food for Thought

A waiter was taking a break. He said to a brand new employee, "You just have to be the one <u>to break the ice</u> with the chef. Sometimes it seems like he has <u>a chip on his shoulder</u>, but he's okay. This is a busy place. You've jumped <u>out of the frying pan and into the fire</u>, let me tell you. I hope you don't have any <u>pie-in-the-sky</u> ideas about taking things easy here. Some days, I feel like I'm <u>going bananas</u>. It might not be your <u>cup of tea</u>. I think we've got <u>the cream of the crop</u> here; everybody does a great job. It's hard sometimes not to <u>fly off the handle</u> when things are so hectic, though. I think you'll do all right if you don't mind hard work."

1. ____d____ to break the ice

2. ____f____ a chip on his shoulder

3. ____h____ out of the frying pan and into the fire

4. ____a____ pie-in-the-sky

5. ____G____ going bananas

6. ____b____ cup of tea

7. ____c____ the cream of the crop

8. ____e____ fly off the handle

A unrealistic

B something one enjoys

C the best available

D to make a start

E to lose one's temper

F seemingly angry or resentful

G go crazy

H from a bad situation to a worse one

STOP

Georgia Test Practice

**English/
Language Arts**

ELA5R3

Words with Multiple Meanings

Clue   If you are not sure which answer is correct, eliminate answers you know are wrong and then take your best guess.

DIRECTIONS: Choose one word from the list that correctly completes both sentences.

1. **The player began to ___a___ .**
   Put the new ___d___ on the car.
   - (A) run
   - (B) fender
   - (C) weaken
   - (D) tire

2. **The sun ___J___ at 5:45 A.M.**
   A ___G___ grew beside the steps.
   - (F) appeared
   - (G) rose
   - (H) flower
   - (J) set

3. **My ___C___ is in the closet.**
   Add a new ___d___ of paint.
   - (A) hat
   - (B) color
   - (C) shirt
   - (D) coat

4. **Do you feel _____ ?**
   We get our water from a _____ .
   - (F) well
   - (G) good
   - (H) pipe
   - (J) sick

5. **Mrs. Johnson said Carrie was a _____ student.**
   The light from the headlights was _____ .
   - (A) noisy
   - (B) red
   - (C) bright
   - (D) hard working

DIRECTIONS: Choose the answer that uses the underlined word from the example in the same way.

6. **Please <u>file</u> these papers.**
   - (F) The counselor pulled out her file on the Jones family.
   - (G) Sally used a file to smooth her fingernails.
   - (H) I put the file cards in order.
   - (J) Jane asked her secretary to file the reports on water safety.

7. **I used a <u>lemon</u> to make lemonade.**
   - (A) The color of the baby's room is lemon.
   - (B) That car was a lemon.
   - (C) This cleaner has a lovely lemon scent.
   - (D) Rachel bought a lemon at the store.

STOP

English/
Language Arts
ELA5R3

Synonyms, Antonyms, and Homophones

Clue

A **synonym** is a word that means the same or nearly the same as another word. An **antonym** is a word that means the opposite of another word. A **homophone** is a word that sounds like another word but has a different meaning and spelling.

DIRECTIONS: Circle the correct homophone in each sentence.

1. We plan to visit Uncle Harry in one *(week, weak)*.

2. Men's jackets are on *(sail, sale)* today.

3. An accident occurred at the track *(meet, meat)*.

4. Cindy's papers *(blew, blue)* away in the wind.

DIRECTIONS: Write three synonyms for each word.

5. pretty: _____ _____ _____

6. hot: _____ _____ _____

DIRECTIONS: Write three antonyms for each word.

7. pretty: _____ _____ _____

8. hot: _____ _____ _____

DIRECTIONS: Choose the word that means the same or about the same as the underlined word.

9. skilled <u>laborer</u>
   - (A) musician
   - (B) professor
   - (C) worker
   - (D) relative

10. An <u>imaginary</u> story is _____ .
    - (F) biographical
    - (G) fictional
    - (H) actual
    - (J) humorous

11. <u>portable</u> grill
    - (A) movable
    - (B) permanent
    - (C) stationery
    - (D) casual

12. <u>vivid</u> color
    - (F) pale
    - (G) without
    - (H) intense
    - (J) soft

DIRECTIONS: Fill in the circle next to the word that means the opposite of the underlined word.

13. <u>brief</u> description
    - (A) important
    - (B) lengthy
    - (C) short
    - (D) casual

14. <u>employ</u> the workers
    - (F) befriend
    - (G) manage
    - (H) argue with
    - (J) dismiss

STOP

Georgia Test Practice

English/
Language Arts

ELA5R4

Using Letter-Sound Knowledge

DIRECTIONS: Choose the best answer.

1. Which word has the same beginning sound as the picture name?

- (A) blast
- (B) share
- (C) clear
- (D) chain

2. Which beginning letter blend is the same as that in the word *plank*?

- (F) blimp
- (G) plate
- (H) clang
- (J) glad

3. Which beginning letter blend is the same as that in the word *trade*?

- (A) grizzly
- (B) frontier
- (C) trowel
- (D) brilliant

4. Which word has the same ending sound as the picture name?

- (F) monsoon
- (G) perform
- (H) journal
- (J) fireproof

5. Which ending sound is the same as that in the word *jitterbug*?

- (A) esophagus
- (B) conservator
- (C) dialogue
- (D) stubborn

6. Which ending sound is the same as that in the word *battle*?

- (F) politics
- (G) cement
- (H) monumental
- (J) sharkskin

7. Which word has the same middle sound as the picture name?

- (A) kitten
- (B) harsh
- (C) diver
- (D) demon

8. Which middle sound is the same as that in the word *camel*?

- (F) seven
- (G) batter
- (H) clipper
- (J) swimmer

STOP

**English/
Language Arts**

ELA5R3–ELA5R4

For pages 36–43

Mini-Test 2

DIRECTIONS: Choose the word that correctly completes both sentences.

1. **Someone bought the _____ on the corner.**

   A new house costs a _____ of money.

   (A) bunch   (C) house

   (B) lot   (D) property

2. **Inez bought a _____ of soda.**

   The doctor said it was a difficult _____ .

   (F) case   (H) disease

   (G) carton   (J) situation

DIRECTIONS: Use the dictionary entry below to answer questions 3–4.

beam [bēm] *n.* **1.** a squared-off log used to support a building **2.** a ray of light **3.** the wooden roller in a loom *v.* **1.** to shine **2.** to smile broadly

3. **Which sentence uses the word *beam* in the same way as the first definition of the noun?**

   (A) The beam held up the plaster ceiling.

   (B) The beam of sunlight warmed the room.

   (C) She moved the beam before she added a row of wool.

   (D) The bright stars beam in the night sky.

4. **The *ea* in the word *beam* sounds most like the *ea* in the word _____ .**

   (F) beautiful   (H) treat

   (G) great   (J) tear

5. **Which sentence contains an idiom?**

   (A) The sunset was a beautiful rainbow of color.

   (B) She heard it straight from the horse's mouth.

   (C) Sasha's memories were like the pages of a book.

   (D) The light flickered and then went out.

DIRECTIONS: Choose the word that means the opposite of the underlined word.

6. express **your thoughts**

   (F) yell

   (G) withhold

   (H) summarize

   (J) tell

7. obvious **signs**

   (A) unclear

   (B) apparent

   (C) momentary

   (D) secondary

DIRECTIONS: Choose the word that means the same or about the same as the underlined word.

8. **Complete the** assignment.

   (F) task

   (G) assistant

   (H) design

   (J) office

9. Focus **your attention.**

   (A) fluctuate

   (B) irritate

   (C) compile

   (D) concentrate

DIRECTIONS: Choose the answer that means the same as the underlined part of the word.

10. reapply rearrange

    (F) opposite of

    (G) full of

    (H) again

    (J) forward

STOP

Writing Standards

The student writes clear, coherent text that develops a central idea or tells a story. The writing shows consideration of the audience and purpose. The student progresses through the stages of the writing process (e.g., prewriting, drafting, revising, and editing successive versions).

ELA5W1. The student produces writing that establishes an appropriate organizational structure, sets a context and engages the reader, maintains a coherent focus throughout, and signals a satisfying closure. *(See page 48.)* **The student:**

a. selects a focus, an organizational structure, and a point of view based on purpose, genre expectations, audience, length, and format requirements.
b. writes texts of an appropriate length to address the topic or tell the story.
c. uses traditional structures for conveying information (e.g., chronological order, cause and effect, similarity and difference, and posing and answering a question).
d. uses appropriate structures to ensure coherence (e.g., transition elements).

ELA5W2. The student demonstrates competence in a variety of genres. *(See pages 49–56.)*

What it means:
- **Genre** is a type, or category, of writing. Some examples of genre include fiction, nonfiction, poetry, and biographies.

The student produces a <u>narrative</u> that:

a. engages the reader by establishing a context, creating a point of view, and otherwise developing reader interest.
b. establishes a plot, point of view, setting, and conflict, and/or the significance of events.
c. creates an organizing structure.
d. includes sensory details and concrete language to develop plot and character.
e. excludes extraneous details and inconsistencies.
f. develops complex characters through actions describing the motivation of characters and character conversation.
g. uses a range of appropriate narrative strategies such as flashback, foreshadowing, dialogue, tension, or suspense.
h. provides a sense of closure to the writing.
i. lifts the level of language using appropriate strategies including word choice.

What it means:
- **Narratives** are stories or events that have a clear beginning, middle, and end. They can be stories about personal or fictional events.

Writing Standards

The student produces <u>informational writing</u> (e.g., report, procedures, correspondence) that:

a. engages the reader by establishing a context, creating a speaker's voice, and otherwise developing reader interest.
b. develops a controlling idea that conveys a perspective on a subject.
c. creates an organizing structure appropriate to a specific purpose, audience, and context.
d. includes appropriate facts and details.
e. excludes extraneous details and inappropriate information.
f. uses a range of appropriate strategies, such as providing facts and details, describing or analyzing the subject, and narrating a relevant anecdote.
g. draws from more than one source of information such as speakers, books, newspapers, and online materials.
h. provides a sense of closure to the writing.
i. lifts the level of language using appropriate strategies including word choice.

What it means:

- **Informational,** or expository, writing conveys information or offers an explanation.

The student produces a <u>response to literature</u> that:

a. engages the reader by establishing a context, creating a speaker's voice, and otherwise developing reader interest.
b. advances a judgment that is interpretive, evaluative, or reflective.
c. supports judgments through references to the text, other works, authors, or nonprint media, or references to personal knowledge.
d. develops interpretations that exhibit careful reading and demonstrates an understanding of the literary work.
e. excludes extraneous details and inappropriate information.
f. provides a sense of closure to the writing.
g. lifts the level of language using appropriate strategies including word choice.

The student produces a <u>persuasive essay</u> that:

a. engages the reader by establishing a context, creating a speaker's voice, and otherwise developing reader interest.
b. states a clear position in support of a proposal.
c. supports a position with relevant evidence.
d. creates an organizing structure appropriate to a specific purpose, audience, and context.
e. addresses reader concerns.
f. excludes extraneous details and inappropriate information.
g. provides a sense of closure to the writing.
h. raises the level of language using appropriate strategies (word choice).

What it means:

- **Persuasive** writing tries to persuade, or convince, the reader about a certain idea.

Writing Standards

ELA5W3. The student uses research and technology to support writing. *(See pages 57–59.)* **The student:**

a. acknowledges information from sources.
b. uses organizational features of printed text (e.g., citations, end notes, bibliographic references) to locate relevant information.
c. uses various reference materials (e.g., dictionary, thesaurus, encyclopedia, electronic information) as aids to writing.
d. uses the features of texts (e.g., index, table of contents, guide words, alphabetical/numerical order) to obtain and organize information and thoughts.
e. demonstrates basic keyboarding skills and familiarity with computer terminology (e.g., software, memory, disk drive, hard drive).
f. creates simple documents by using electronic media and employing organizational features (e.g., passwords, entry and pull-down menus, word searches, thesaurus, spell check).
g. uses a thesaurus to identify alternative word choices and meanings.

ELA5W4. The student consistently uses a writing process to develop, revise, and evaluate writing. *(See page 60.)* **The student:**

a. plans and drafts independently and resourcefully.
b. revises manuscripts to improve the meaning and focus of writing by adding, deleting, consolidating, clarifying, and rearranging words and sentences.
c. edits to correct errors in spelling, punctuation, etc.

English/
Language Arts
ELA5W1

Matching Structure to Purpose

DIRECTIONS: Read the paragraph below about how to plant a seed. Then think of something you know how to do well. Write a paragraph to your classmates that explains how to do it. Keep your audience in mind as you write your paragraph. Use transition words such as *first, next, then, finally,* and *last.* Use details to explain how you learned to do this activity and why you enjoy it.

> I found out how to plant a seed and make it grow. First, I found a spot where the plant would get the right amount of sunlight. Next, I dug a hole, put the seed into the soil, and then covered the seed with soil. Then I watered the seed. After a couple weeks, it began to grow into a beautiful plant.

_____
_____
_____
_____
_____
_____
_____
_____
_____
_____
_____
_____
_____
_____
_____
_____
_____
_____

STOP

Name _____   Date _____

Writing Narratives

DIRECTIONS: Think of a topic for a short story. To help you write it, complete the following.

1. What is the plot of the story?

_____

_____

_____

_____

_____

_____

2. Describe the setting of the story.

_____

_____

_____

_____

_____

_____

3. Who are the characters?

_____

_____

_____

_____

4. What words would you use to describe the characters?

_____

_____

_____

_____

_____

_____

_____

5. What is the point of view of the story?

_____

_____

_____

_____

_____

_____

_____

Name _____ Date _____

DIRECTIONS: Now write your short story. Use the plot, setting, characters, and point of view that you brainstormed. Remember to include sensory details to develop your characters.

6. _____

_____

_____

_____

_____

_____

_____

_____

_____

_____

_____

_____

_____

_____

_____

_____

_____

_____

_____

_____

_____

_____

_____

_____

_____

_____

_____

_____

_____

STOP

Name _____ Date _____

Informational Writing

DIRECTIONS: Write a composition responding to the following question: Do you think there is too much violence on TV, in the movies, and in video games? Answer the following questions to organize your information.

1. **What do you think are the effects of showing violence on TV, in the movies, and in video games?**

   _____

   _____

   _____

   _____

   _____

   _____

2. **Find graphs, charts, or other visuals that give you information about the topic. What information do they provide? Include the graphs and charts with your composition.**

   _____

   _____

   _____

   _____

   _____

   _____

3. **What sources did you use to find more information on the topic?**

   _____

   _____

   _____

   _____

   _____

   _____

4. **What are possible solutions to the problem?**

   _____

   _____

   _____

   _____

   _____

   _____

GO

DIRECTIONS: Now write the informational composition. Remember to clearly state your purpose for writing, develop your topic with supporting details, and conclude with a detailed summary.

5. _____

_____

_____

_____

_____

_____

_____

_____

_____

_____

_____

_____

_____

_____

_____

_____

_____

_____

_____

_____

_____

_____

_____

_____

_____

_____

_____

_____

STOP

Responding to Literature

The Escape

Into the shady glen, the small figure rode on a pony that was little larger than a dog. The pony's breath misted in the crisp air as the beast blew air out of its nostrils. The green-mantled figure patted the neck of the beast, whispering words of comfort into the animal's ear. In response, the faithful steed nickered, thumped his wide hoofs twice upon the soft bed of the forest floor, and ceased its shaking.

"We've left the raiders behind, old friend," said Rowan, as she removed her hooded mantle and tossed her head back and forth, bringing peace to her own troubled mind. Rowan was one of four daughters of Sylvia, guide of all wood folk.

Suddenly, shouts of rough men cut through the glade's peace.

"In here, I tell ya. The maid's gone to hiding in this grove."

"Nah, ya lunk. She'd never wait for us here. Not after she dunked old Stefan at the marsh. No! She's a gone on to her crazy folk, don'tcha know."

The two gray-cloaked riders dismounted, still arguing as they examined the earth for traces of the child's flight.

"Who was the lout who let her escape?" asked the first.

"'Tis one who no longer breathes the air so freely," returned the second grimly. "The lord nearly choked the fool, even as the knave begged for mercy. Ah, there's little patience for one who lets a mystic escape, to be true!"

Five nobly dressed horsemen wove through the trees to the clearing where these two rustics still squatted. In the lead came the fierce lord, a huge form with scarlet and gray finery worn over his coat of mail.

"What say you?" he roared. "Have you found the trail of Rowan?"

"No, sire," spoke the first gray, trembling, "though I was certain the child headed into this wood. Shall I continue to search, lord?"

"Aye, indeed," replied the master calmly, controlled. "She is here. I know it, too. You have a keen sense for the hunt, Mikkel. Be at ready with your blade. And you too, Short Brush! Though a child, our Rowan is vicious with her weapon."

"Yes, sire," agreed Mikkel and Short Brush.

The two grays beat the bushes in the search. Closer and closer they came to the child's hiding place, a small earthen scoop created when the roots of a wind-blown tree pulled free of the earth.

The evil lord and his lot remained mounted, ready to pursue should the young girl determine to take flight once more. And so, they were not prepared for the child's play.

Rowan softly, softly sang, "You wind-whipped branches shudder, shake. You oaks and cedars, tremble. Take these men and beasts who do us wrong. Not in these woods do they belong."

As a mighty gust of wind roared, nearby trees slapped their branches to the point of breaking, reaching out and grasping the five mounted men. An immense gaping cavern opened in the trunk of an ancient oak and swallowed the five surprised mail-clad men whole.

Mikkel and Short Brush, too, were lifted high into the air by a white pine and a blue spruce. Lifted high. Kept high. For a while.

"Return from whence you came. Go to your families, and tell them of the wrath of Sylvia," commanded Rowan. "She would not wish you to come to her land again!"

The pine and spruce tossed the two gray trackers over the trees of the forest and into the field beyond. The field was already harvested and soggy with the rains of autumn. Mikkel and Short Brush, unhurt but shaken by their arboreal flight, rose and fled immediately to tell their master of the strange doings of this wood.

GO ➡

Name _____ Date _____

DIRECTIONS: Read the story on the previous page and then answer the questions.

1. Where do you think this story takes place? Cite evidence from the story to support your answers.

_____

_____

_____

_____

2. How would you describe the dialect (the way the characters talk) in this story? Based on the way the characters speak, how do you imagine they are dressed?

_____

_____

_____

_____

3. What details tell the reader that Rowan is very small?

_____

_____

_____

_____

4. What details help you picture the fierce lord?

_____

_____

_____

_____

5. Why do you think Rowan was trying to escape? Support your answer with references to the text.

_____

_____

_____

_____

STOP

English/
Language Arts

ELA5W2

Writing to Persuade

DIRECTIONS: Read the passage. Then complete the Venn diagram and answer the questions on the next page.

Cross-Country or Downhill?

The answer to this question makes a big difference if you are a skier. Both forms of skiing are popular and can be done by people of all ages. Both require snow, and both can be done for relaxation or competition. So what is it that makes the two methods of skiing so different?

Cross-country skiing means just that— you ski across the country. You do not need tall hills or ski lifts to ski cross-country. You simply need snow and equipment. Cross-country skiers can go skiing right outside their back door. Even land that is completely flat can be enjoyable for the cross-country skier. Cross-country races can be 50 minutes long or two hours long. These long races require strength and endurance. Races vary in length from 9 miles to 30 miles.

Downhill skiing is also named for the activity. A downhill skier skis down hills. That means the skier needs tall hills and a way to get up to the top. Downhill skiing takes place at ski resorts. Downhill races are short. The goal is to get down the hill the fastest without falling. Speed is the goal, and downhill racers can go faster than 80 miles per hour.

Both types of skiing require special equipment. Downhill skis are wider and shorter than cross-country skis. The boots are also different. Downhill boots are larger and protect the ankles from injury. They are connected to the ski at the heel and toe with a binding. Cross-country boots are flexible, like shoes, and usually fit below the ankle. They are attached to the ski at the toe only. Both types of skiing require ski poles. A downhill skier uses poles for balance and direction, whereas a cross-country skier uses poles as part of the glide-step technique.

Both forms of skiing are great exercise, but cross-country skiing has the potential to burn more calories. Cross-country skiing at a pace of 5 to 8 miles an hour can burn 9 to 13 calories per minute. Downhill skiing at a moderate pace burns 6 calories per minute. No matter which form of skiing you choose, you will be doing something good for your body.

GO

Name _____ Date _____

1. **Complete the Venn diagram below, listing the similarities and differences between cross-country and downhill skiing.**

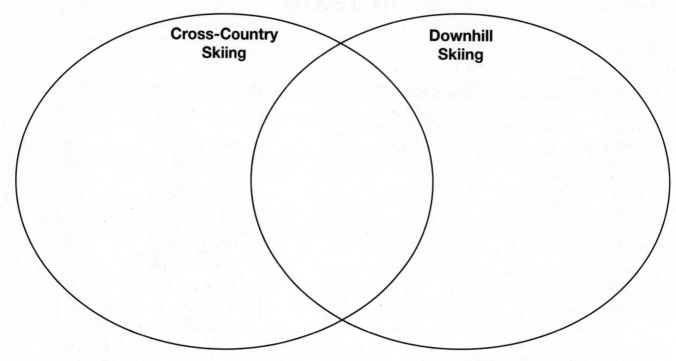

2. **Which type of skiing is easiest to do? Explain your answer. Use facts from the diagram to support your opinion.**

_____

_____

_____

_____

_____

_____

_____

3. **Which type of skiing is the most expensive? Explain your answer. Use facts from the diagram to support your opinion.**

_____

_____

_____

_____

_____

_____

_____

STOP

English/
Language Arts

ELA5W3

Locating Information in Texts

DIRECTIONS: Choose the best answer.

1. **In doing her research for a report, Wanda used the book titled *Technology Tomorrow*. Where in the book should Wanda look to learn what information is found in each chapter?**

   Ⓐ the index

   Ⓑ the table of contents

   Ⓒ the title page

   Ⓓ the introduction

2. **Where in the book should Wanda look to learn when the book was published?**

   Ⓕ the index

   Ⓖ the table of contents

   Ⓗ the copyright page

   Ⓙ the bibliography

3. **Where in the book should Wanda look to learn what other sources she might be able to use for her report?**

   Ⓐ the index

   Ⓑ the table of contents

   Ⓒ the title page

   Ⓓ the bibliography

4. **Because Wanda has used other sources to write her report, she should _____ .**

   Ⓕ explain in her introduction that she has used other sources

   Ⓖ make photocopies of her sources and attach them to her report

   Ⓗ acknowledge her sources in citations and a bibliography

   Ⓙ ignore the sources because she is only writing a report for school

---

Index

Engines
fuel, 32–36
types of, 30–38

History
in Africa, 18–22
in Asia, 20–24
in Europe, 2–10
in North America, 8–18
in South America, 16–18
legends and stories, 72–78

Tracks
laying, 26–32
types, 28–33, 93–95

Workers
job classifications, 80–85
unions, 4–8

---

5. **The index above appears in a book about trains. Which pages would probably tell about a Ghost Train some people say they have seen?**

   Ⓐ 72–78

   Ⓑ 32–36

   Ⓒ 80–85

   Ⓓ 28–33

6. **Which pages would give you information on trains that ran between France and Germany during the 1930s?**

   Ⓕ 4–8

   Ⓖ 18–22

   Ⓗ 2–10

   Ⓙ 16–18

Using Reference Materials

DIRECTIONS: Use the sample thesaurus entry below to answer the questions.

> **supine** [sŭ-`pīn] *adj.* **1.** flat, flat on one's
> back, horizontal, lounging, recline
> **2.** inactive, motionless, lazy, lifeless
> **supple** [`sə-pəl] *adj.* **1.** flexible, bendable,
> pliant; elastic, stretchable **2.** limber,
> loose-limbed, double-jointed
> **3.** yielding, unresistant, passive
> **4.** changeable, movable, agreeable,
> willing

1. **The words listed in this thesaurus entry are both _____ .**

   (A) nouns

   (B) verbs

   (C) adjectives

   (D) adverbs

2. **Write three synonyms for the word *supple*.**

   _____

   _____

3. **Write one antonym for the word *supple*.**

   _____

4. **Even if you didn't know the meaning of *supine* before looking in the thesaurus, how would you define it after reading this entry? Write a definition.**

   _____

   _____

   _____

DIRECTIONS: A **bibliography** is a list of the books and articles a writer uses for reference when writing a report. A bibliography tells interested readers where to find more information on the report's topic. The bibliography below was prepared by someone who wrote a report called *The Wild West.* Read the bibliography and use it to answer questions 5–9.

> **Book**
> Alter, Judy. Author
> *Growing Up in the Old West*
> Watts, 1999
>
> **Encyclopedia Article**
> "Pioneers in the Wild West"
> *McMahon Encyclopedia*, 2002 edition
> vol. 12, pp. 278–282.
>
> **Magazine Article**
> Tripp, John R. Author
> "Exploring the American West."
> *The U.S. Experience*
> vol. 114 (April 1998): 25–32.

5. **What three types of references did the writer use to write her report?**

   _____

   _____

   _____

6. **Which of these references was published most recently?**

   _____

7. **In what volume of the encyclopedia did the writer find her information about pioneers in the Wild West?**

   _____

8. On what pages did the magazine article appear?

_____

9. If you wanted to find out what it was like to be a child in the Old West, what would be the best reference?

_____

DIRECTIONS: Use the sample dictionary entries and the Pronunciation Guide to answer questions 10–15.

---

camp [kamp´] *n.* **1.** a place, usually away from cities, where tents or simple buildings are put up to provide shelter for people working or vacationing there **2.** a place, usually in the country, for recreation or instruction during the summer months [goes to summer camp each July] **3.** a group of people who work to promote a certain idea or thought or who work together in support of another person *v.* **4.** to live temporarily in a camp or outdoors
cam·paign [kam-pān´] *n.* **1.** a series of military operations that make up a distinct period during a war **2.** a series of activities designed to bring about a desired outcome [an election campaign] *v.* **3.** to conduct a campaign
cam·pus [kam´-pəs] *n.* **1.** the grounds and buildings of a school

Pronunciation Guide:
ash, st**ay**, ə = a in *alone* and u in *circus*, w**e**t, **e**asy, h**i**t, h**i**de, f**o**x, g**o**, b**u**t, m**u**sic

---

10. The "u" in *campus* sounds most like the vowel sound in _____ .

   (F) but
   (G) music
   (H) circus
   (J) wet

11. Which definition best fits the word *camp* as it is used in the sentence below?

   The field workers lived in a *camp* a mile away from the farm.

   (A) 1
   (B) 2
   (C) 3
   (D) 4

12. How many syllables are in the word *campaign?*

   (F) 1
   (G) 2
   (H) 3
   (J) 4

13. In which of these sentences is *camp* used as a verb?

   (A) The governor's camp worked through the night to prepare her acceptance speech.
   (B) Della will go to music camp in July.
   (C) The hike back to camp took three hours.
   (D) The family will camp in Yosemite this spring.

14. What part of speech is the word *campus?*

   (F) verb
   (G) noun
   (H) adjective
   (J) adverb

15. Look at the words in the sample dictionary. Which guide words would appear on the dictionary page on which these words are located?

   (A) campground–candle
   (B) camera–campfire
   (C) camisole–canal
   (D) camper–campsite

STOP

Name _____ Date _____

Adding and Deleting Text

DIRECTIONS: Read the report, and then answer the questions.

(1) Thomas Jefferson accomplished many great things. (2) He is probably best known as the main author of the Declaration of Independence. (3) Jefferson was a person of integrity, and many people trusted him. (4) He was a member of the Continental Congress and a minister to France. (5) He was made Secretary of State in 1790 and vice president in 1797. (6) Jefferson served as President of the United States from 1801 to 1809. (7) His wife was not alive to be his first lady. (8) This great man continued to work for his principles until he passed away in 1826.

1. **What is the topic sentence of the paragraph?**

   (A) sentence 1

   (B) sentence 2

   (C) sentence 3

   (D) sentence 4

2. **Which of these could be added after sentence 2?**

   (F) Many politicians signed the Declaration.

   (G) He was only 33 years old when he helped write the Declaration.

   (H) The Declaration of Independence was the first step in a war against Britain.

   (J) Benjamin Franklin helped Jefferson with some of the ideas in the document.

3. **Which sentence does not belong in the paragraph?**

   (A) sentence 5

   (B) sentence 6

   (C) sentence 7

   (D) sentence 8

4. **Which of these could be added after sentence 6?**

   (F) He was president for seven years.

   (G) During his presidency, he helped the United States purchase the Louisiana Territories.

   (H) Some people liked him and some didn't.

   (J) He was only the eighth president of the United States.

5. **Write a sentence 9 to complete the paragraph.**

   _____

   _____

   _____

   _____

   _____

   _____

   _____

English/
Language Arts

Mini-Test 3

ELA5W1–ELA5W4

For pages 48–60

DIRECTIONS: Read the paragraph. Choose the sentence that does not belong.

1.   (1) Niagara Falls, one of the world's biggest waterfalls, is partly in the United States and partly in Canada. (2) My family went there for our vacation last summer. (3) In 1969, scientists did a strange thing at the falls. (4) They shut off the American falls for several months by building a big dam across the river so no water could get to the falls. (5) The scientists wanted to study the rocks underneath the water.

  Ⓐ sentence 1
  Ⓑ sentence 2
  Ⓒ sentence 4
  Ⓓ sentence 5

DIRECTIONS: Read the paragraph. Choose the sentence that fits best in the blank.

2.   One of the nicest things about summer evenings is being able to watch fireflies or try to catch them. _____ Some scientists think the lights are used to scare away birds that might eat the fireflies. Others think the fireflies use their lights to say "Hello" to their future mates.

  Ⓕ My grandma likes to sit on the porch in the evening.
  Ⓖ I usually catch fireflies in a big jar.
  Ⓗ Fireflies need to have lots of air if you catch them and put them in a jar.
  Ⓙ Did you ever wonder why fireflies light up?

DIRECTIONS: Use the index below to answer question 3.

```
┌─────────────────────────────────┐
│            Index                │
│  aspirin, 41, 170               │
│  brain, 171                     │
│  calcium, 53, 193               │
│  eardrums, 179                  │
│  food allergies, 39, 167        │
│  insect bites, 48, 183          │
│  lips, 179                      │
└─────────────────────────────────┘
```

3. On which page would you find information about why some people cannot eat nuts?
  Ⓐ page 48   Ⓒ page 193
  Ⓑ page 171   Ⓓ page 39

DIRECTIONS: Choose the best answer.

4. Where would you find information about the sources an author used to write a book?
  Ⓕ title page   Ⓗ bibliography
  Ⓖ index   Ⓙ table of contents

5. If you wanted to find a synonym for the word *attractive,* which reference would you use?
  Ⓐ a dictionary
  Ⓑ an encyclopedia
  Ⓒ an atlas
  Ⓓ a thesaurus

6. You want to write about an adventure two friends have while hiking in the mountains. What type of writing will you use?
  Ⓕ persuasive writing
  Ⓖ informational writing
  Ⓗ response to literature
  Ⓙ narrative writing

GO

DIRECTIONS: Write a paragraph about the funniest thing that has ever happened to you. Give details that will help the readers feel like they were there, too.

7. _____

_____

_____

_____

_____

_____

_____

_____

_____

_____

_____

_____

_____

_____

_____

_____

_____

_____

_____

_____

_____

_____

DIRECTIONS: Think of your favorite sport or game. Write a paragraph that explains how to play it. Use transition words such as *first, next, then,* and *last.*

8. _____

_____

_____

_____

_____

_____

_____

DIRECTIONS: Write a paragraph to persuade your teacher to take your class on an outing to a local amusement park.

9. _____

_____

_____

_____

_____

_____

_____

_____

_____

_____

_____

_____

_____

_____

_____

_____

STOP

Conventions Standards

Conventions are essential for reading, writing, and speaking. Instruction in language conventions will, therefore, occur within the context of reading, writing, and speaking, rather than in isolation. The student writes to make connections with the larger world. A student's ideas are more likely to be taken seriously when the words are spelled accurately and the sentences are grammatically correct. Use of Standard English conventions helps readers understand and follow the student's meaning, while errors can be distracting and confusing. Standard English conventions are the "good manners" of writing and speaking that make communication fluid.

ELA5C1. The student demonstrates understanding and control of the rules of the English language, realizing that usage involves the appropriate application of conventions and grammar in both written and spoken formats. *(See pages 64–69.)* **The student:**

a. uses and identifies the eight parts of speech (e.g., noun, pronoun, verb, adverb, adjective, conjunction, preposition, interjection).
b. expands or reduces sentences (e.g., adding or deleting modifiers, combining or revising sentences).
c. uses and identifies verb phrases and verb tenses.
d. recognizes that a word performs different functions according to its position in the sentence.
e. varies the sentence structure by kind (declarative, interrogative, imperative, and exclamatory sentences and functional fragments), order, and complexity (simple, compound, complex, and compound-complex).

What it means:
- A **declarative** sentence makes a statement.
- An **interrogative** sentence asks a question.
- An **imperative** sentence expresses a command or request.
- An **exclamatory** sentence shows excitement or emotion.
- A **simple** sentence has one independent clause and no dependent clause.
- A **compound sentence** has two or more independent clauses and no dependent clause.
- A **complex** sentence has one independent clause and one dependent clause.
- A **compound-complex** sentence has two or more independent clauses and at least one dependent clause.

f. uses and identifies correct mechanics (e.g., apostrophes, quotation marks, comma use in compound sentences, paragraph indentations) and correct sentence structure (e.g., elimination of sentence fragments and run-ons).
g. uses additional knowledge of correct mechanics (e.g., apostrophes, quotation marks, comma use in compound sentences, paragraph indentations), correct sentence structure (e.g., elimination of fragments and run-ons), and correct Standard English spelling (e.g., commonly-used homophones) when writing, revising, and editing.

**English/
Language Arts**

ELA5C1

Identifying
Parts of Speech

DIRECTIONS: Read the passage below. Write the part of speech under each underlined word. Use **N** (noun), **PRON** (pronoun), **V** (verb), **ADJ** (adjective), **ADV** (adverb), **PREP** (preposition), **C** (conjunction), or **I** (interjection).

Nouns:	name people (*Ann*), places (*Chicago*), things (*car*), or ideas (*creation*)
Pronouns:	rename nouns (*she, he, it*)
Verbs:	express action (*run*) or a state of being (*is*)
Adverbs:	modify verbs (*slowly* running), adjectives (*more* efficient car), or other adverbs (*relatively* quickly)
Adjectives:	describe or modify nouns (*red* car) or pronouns (She is *tired*.)
Prepositions:	express relationships between nouns or pronouns and other words (*in* the dark, *after* him, *down* the stairs)
Conjunctions:	connect words to each other (*and, or, but, while*)
Interjections:	express surprise or emotion and are usually followed by an exclamation mark (*Oh! Hey! Wow!*)

Let's Go Swimming

"You <u>said</u> there was a <u>river</u> near here. Why don't we go swimming?" suggested

<u>Mara</u>, wiping the sweat off her brow.

"<u>Oh</u>! <u>You</u> wouldn't want to swim in that river!" said Eva.

"Why not?" Mara asked. "I'm a <u>strong</u> <u>swimmer</u>. Even if the river's deep <u>or</u> the

current's fast, <u>it</u> won't <u>bother</u> me."

"It's not that the river is deep or <u>fast</u>," said Eva. "If you <u>like</u> swimming <u>with</u> tires,

broken <u>bottles</u>, and <u>rusty</u> cans, you can swim there."

"Well," said Mara, "I don't <u>think</u> I want to swim that <u>badly</u>. Isn't there a public

pool in town?"

STOP

Georgia Test Practice

**English/
Language Arts**

ELA5C1

Conventions

Expanding and Combining Sentences

DIRECTIONS: Complete each sentence. Use the conjunctions *and*, *or*, *for*, or *but* after the comma. Use a different conjunction in each sentence. The second part must contain a subject and a predicate.

1. The sky is blue,

_____

_____

2. My father went shopping,

_____

_____

3. The doorbell rang,

_____

_____

DIRECTIONS: Choose the answer that best combines the underlined sentences.

4. <u>The window is locked. The door is locked.</u>

- Ⓐ The door is locked and the window.
- Ⓑ The door and window is locked.
- Ⓒ The window is locked, and the door.
- Ⓓ The window and door are locked.

5. <u>The television is plugged in. The television still isn't working.</u>

- Ⓕ If the television is plugged in, it still won't work.
- Ⓖ The television still isn't working because it is plugged in.
- Ⓗ Because the television is still plugged in, it isn't working.
- Ⓙ The television is plugged in, but it still isn't working.

DIRECTIONS: Read the story. Then answer the questions.

(1) Last Saturday, the Wilson family drove to Chicago to watch a Cubs baseball game. **(2)** The bustling streets around the ballpark were filled with activity. **(3)** The children spotted a booth outside the stadium that was selling Cubs' baseball caps. **(4)** They begged their dad to buy them hats. **(5)** He insisted that they wait until they got inside the park. **(6)** When they got to the front of the line, the children saw a woman handing out free Cubs' hats. **(7)** It was free hat day. **(8)** Mr. Wilson smiled and the children cheered.

6. How is sentence 1 best written?

- Ⓐ On a drive to Chicago last Saturday, the Wilson family was watching a Cubs baseball game.
- Ⓑ To watch a Cubs baseball game, the Wilson family drove to Chicago.
- Ⓒ Last Saturday, the Wilson family was driving to Chicago and watching a Cubs baseball game.
- Ⓓ as it is

7. What is the best way to combine sentences 4 and 5 without changing their meaning?

- Ⓕ They begged their dad to buy them hats, but he insisted that they wait until they got inside the park.
- Ⓖ They begged their dad to buy them hats, because he insisted that they wait until they got inside the park.
- Ⓗ They begged their dad to buy them hats; therefore, he insisted that they wait until they got inside the park.
- Ⓙ Since their dad insisted that they wait until they got inside the park, they begged him to buy them hats.

English/
Language Arts

ELA5C1

Using a Variety of Sentence Structures

DIRECTIONS: Below are four short paragraphs. For each paragraph, underline the declarative sentences. Then in each blank, write **IN** if the paragraph also contains an interrogative sentence; write **EX** if it contains an exclamatory sentence; write **IM** if it contains an imperative sentence; write **NONE** if it contains only declarative sentences.

1. _____ You are on a deserted island: no town, no people—just you and those crazy, noisy seagulls. What are you going to do?

2. _____ I think Mama forgot me. Otherwise, she would come and find me. Oh, no! I've been bad! Mama said not to go see the toys because I'd get lost. Mama is going to be mad at me!

3. _____ Maggie bit her lip. There was no use crying about it. She pulled her math homework out of the sink and just stared at her little sister.

4. _____ Do not stop reading until you reach the end of this story. What you are about to read is so amazing that you simply *must* hear about it now. So settle back and get ready for the most incredible tale you've ever heard.

DIRECTIONS: Write *simple* on the line after the simple sentences, *compound* on the line after the compound sentences, and *complex* on the line after the complex sentences.

> A *simple* sentence has one independent clause and no dependent clause. Example: They went to the park and fed the ducks.
>
> A *compound* sentence has two or more independent clauses and no dependent clause. Example: They went to the park, and the ducks wanted food.
>
> A *complex* sentence has one independent clause and one dependent clause. Example: When they entered the park, the ducks flew away.

5. It was a beautiful day, and I was ready for adventure.

_____

6. Because my friend Marcy likes to skate, I invited her to come with me.

_____

7. She strapped on her skates and joined me.

_____

8. Marcy and I enjoyed our trip to the park.

_____

9. When we reached the park, we took a rest.

_____

10. Marcy is new to skating, but I'm not.

_____

Georgia Test Practice

English/Language Arts

ELA5C1

Eliminating Sentence Fragments and Run-Ons

DIRECTIONS: Rewrite each run-on sentence to make it correct. Write *C* if the sentences below are correct as is.

1. Let's ask David to come with us. He knows about a great bike trail.

_____

_____

2. I can ride faster than you can let's race to the stop sign.

_____

_____

3. I'm thirsty does anyone have some bottled water?

_____

_____

4. We need to be careful on the bike trail in-line skaters can appear fast.

_____

_____

5. Do you know how to recognize a happy bicyclist? He has bugs in his teeth.

_____

_____

6. I love the playground it has great swings.

_____

_____

7. When I swing too high, I get sick do you?

_____

_____

8. I like the slide the best. I've always liked slides.

_____

_____

9. This ride was fun let's do it again tomorrow.

_____

_____

DIRECTIONS: Rewrite each sentence fragment below to make it a sentence.

10. found a hidden staircase in the old house

_____

_____

11. a mysterious note

_____

_____

12. lay behind the creaking door

_____

_____

13. the solution to the mystery

_____

_____

STOP

**English/
Language Arts**

ELA5C1

Using Correct
Punctuation and Spelling

DIRECTIONS: Fill in the circle next to the punctuation mark that is needed in the sentence. Choose "none" if no additional punctuation marks are needed.

1. **The team carried in the bats balls, and gloves.**
   - Ⓐ ;
   - Ⓑ ,
   - Ⓒ :
   - Ⓓ none

2. **"Great catch" yelled the pitcher.**
   - Ⓕ ?
   - Ⓖ .
   - Ⓗ !
   - Ⓙ none

3. **Did you see that foul ball**
   - Ⓐ ?
   - Ⓑ .
   - Ⓒ ,
   - Ⓓ none

4. **Matilda hit a home run.**
   - Ⓕ !
   - Ⓖ "
   - Ⓗ ,
   - Ⓙ none

5. **That's three strikes," said the umpire.**
   - Ⓐ ,
   - Ⓑ "
   - Ⓒ "
   - Ⓓ none

6. **Yes the Fifth Grade Firecrackers won the game.**
   - Ⓕ ,
   - Ⓖ .
   - Ⓗ !
   - Ⓙ none

DIRECTIONS: Fill in the blank with the word that best fits each sentence.

7. **Nikki _____ the class in singing the national anthem.**

   led, lead

8. **Show Brendan _____ we keep the extra towels.**

   where, wear

9. **Jamal, the social studies report is**

   _____ tomorrow!

   do, dew, due

10. **Call me when _____ my turn to use the computer.**

    it's, its

11. **We can rest when _____ is nothing left to put away.**

    their, there, they're

12. **The keys were _____ on the table this morning.**

    here, hear

13. **Remember, _____ responsible for returning the videos.**

    your, you're

14. **Nathan _____ a chapter of the book every day after dinner.**

    red, read

15. **Aunt Jess _____ the package to me on Monday.**

    sent, cent, scent

STOP

**English/
Language Arts**

ELA5C1

For pages 64–68

Mini-Test 4

DIRECTIONS: Write the part of speech under each underlined word in the sentence below. Use **N** (noun), **PRON** (pronoun), **PREP** (preposition), **V** (verb), **ADJ** (adjective), **ADV** (adverb), **C** (conjunction), and **I** (interjection).

     (1)   (2)   (3)   (4)
"<u>Wow!</u>" <u>she</u> said as she <u>jumped</u> into the <u>cold</u> water

  (5)   (6)   (7)   (8)
<u>and</u> swam <u>quickly</u> <u>across</u> the <u>pond</u>.

DIRECTIONS: Circle the word that best fits each sentence.

9. The car is parked in (it's, its) usual place.

10. (Their, There, They're) going to be here any minute!

11. What shoes are you going to (where, wear) today?

DIRECTIONS: For numbers 12–14, indicate the correct sentence type.

12. **What are you going to buy your mother for her birthday?**
    - Ⓐ declarative
    - Ⓑ interrogative
    - Ⓒ exclamatory
    - Ⓓ imperative

13. **Please report to my office immediately.**
    - Ⓕ declarative
    - Ⓖ interrogative
    - Ⓗ exclamatory
    - Ⓙ imperative

14. **I really like movies, but Angie prefers shopping.**
    - Ⓐ simple
    - Ⓑ compound
    - Ⓒ complex
    - Ⓓ fragment

DIRECTIONS: Choose the answer that best combines the sentences.

15. **Please go to the refrigerator.**
    I would like you to get a soda for me.
    - Ⓕ Please go to the refrigerator to get a soda for me.
    - Ⓖ Please go to the refrigerator and get me a soda, because I want one.
    - Ⓗ For me, please go to the refrigerator to get a soda.
    - Ⓙ I would like for you to please go to the refrigerator to get a soda for me.

DIRECTIONS: Fill in the circle next to the sentence that is complete and written with correct punctuation.

16.
    - Ⓐ I need to go home can anybody give me a ride?
    - Ⓑ He placed leaves grass and small twigs inside.
    - Ⓒ I watched the hamster playing inside its cage.
    - Ⓓ running in its wheel.

Listening, Speaking, and Viewing Standards

The student demonstrates an understanding of listening, speaking, and viewing skills for a variety of purposes. The student listens critically and responds appropriately to oral communication in a variety of genres and media. The student speaks in a manner that guides the listener to understand important ideas.

ELA5LSV1. The student participates in student-to-teacher, student-to-student, and group verbal interactions. The student:
a. initiates new topics in addition to responding to adult-initiated topics.
b. asks relevant questions.
c. responds to questions with appropriate information.
d. uses language cues to indicate different levels of certainty or hypothesizing (e.g., "What if . . ."; "Very likely . . ."; "I'm unsure whether . . .").
e. confirms understanding by paraphrasing the adult's directions or suggestions.
f. displays appropriate turn-taking behaviors.
g. actively solicits another person's comments or opinions.
h. offers own opinion assertively without domineering.
i. responds appropriately to comments and questions.
j. volunteers contributions and responds when directly solicited by teacher or discussion leader.
k. gives reasons in support of opinions expressed.
l. clarifies, illustrates, or expands on a response when asked to do so; asks classmates for similar expansions.

ELA5LSV2. The student listens to and views various forms of text and media in order to gather and share information, persuade others, and express and understand ideas.
When responding to <u>visual and oral texts and media</u> (e.g., television, radio, film productions, and electronic media), the student:
a. demonstrates an awareness of the presence of the media in the daily lives of most people.
b. evaluates the role of the media in focusing attention and in forming an opinion.
c. judges the extent to which media provide a source of entertainment as well as a source of information.

When delivering or responding to <u>presentations</u>, the student:
a. shapes information to achieve a particular purpose and to appeal to the interests and background knowledge of audience members.
b. uses notes, multimedia, or other memory aids to structure the presentation.
c. engages the audience with appropriate verbal cues and eye contact.
d. projects a sense of individuality and personality in selecting and organizing content and in delivery.
e. shapes content and organization according to criteria for importance and impact rather than according to availability of information in resource materials.
f. uses technology or other memory aids to structure the presentation.

How Am I Doing?

Mini-Test 1

Pages 32–33

Number Correct

10–12 answers correct	**Great Job!** Move on to the section test on page 73.
7–9 answers correct	**You're almost there!** But you still need a little practice. Review practice pages 8–31 before moving on to the section test on page 73.
0–6 answers correct	**Oops!** Time to review what you have learned and try again. Review the practice section on pages 8–31. Then retake the test on pages 32–33. Now move on to the section test on page 73.

Mini-Test 2

Page 44

Number Correct

9–10 answers correct	**Awesome!** Move on to the section test on page 73.
6–8 answers correct	**You're almost there!** But you still need a little practice. Review practice pages 36–43 before moving on to the section test on page 73.
0–5 answers correct	**Oops!** Time to review what you have learned and try again. Review the practice section on pages 36–43. Then retake the test on page 44. Now move on to the section test on page 73.

Mini-Test 3

Pages 61–62

Number Correct

8–9 answers correct	**Great Job!** Move on to the section test on page 73.
5–7 answers correct	**You're almost there!** But you still need a little practice. Review practice pages 48–60 before moving on to the section test on page 73.
0–4 answers correct	**Oops!** Time to review what you have learned and try again. Review the practice section on pages 48–60. Then retake the test on pages 61–62. Now move on to the section test on page 73.

How Am I Doing?

Mini-Test 4	13–16 answers correct	**Awesome!** Move on to the section test on page 73.
Page 69 **Number Correct**	9–12 answers correct	**You're almost there!** But you still need a little practice. Review practice pages 64–68 before moving on to the section test on page 73.
	0–8 answers correct	**Oops!** Time to review what you have learned and try again. Review the practice section on pages 64–68. Then retake the test on page 69. Now move on to the section test on page 73.

Final English/Language Arts Test
for pages 8–68

DIRECTIONS: Read the passage below and then answer the questions that follow.

Act I, Scene 1

Cheryl enters the room carrying her lunch tray and sits across the table from her friend Heather.
CHERYL: Heather, I need an objective opinion. Tracy says I'm a liar.
HEATHER: *(crunching a carrot)* About what?
CHERYL: It doesn't matter. I'm honest, right?
HEATHER: Honest about what?
CHERYL: *(smiling)* You know, trustworthy, direct, truthful.
HEATHER: Well . . . *(hesitating)* Now don't fly off the handle, Cheryl, but what about the time you lied to your folks about your math grade?
CHERYL: Math grades don't count.

1. This passage is an example of what genre?

- (A) short story
- (B) play
- (C) poem
- (D) fable

2. What is the setting of this passage?

- (F) a classroom
- (G) a school cafeteria
- (H) a gymnasium
- (J) a library

3. Based on Heather's response, which adjectives best describe Cheryl?

- (A) honest and objective
- (B) truthful and direct
- (C) dishonest and deceptive
- (D) open and trustworthy

4. The phrase *crunching a carrot* is an example of _____ .

- (F) a simile
- (G) a metaphor
- (H) hyperbole
- (J) onomatopoeia

5. The phrase *fly off the handle* is _____ .

- (A) an idiom
- (B) a simile
- (C) alliteration
- (D) personification

DIRECTIONS: Read the paragraph below and then answer the questions that follow.

An urban habitat is home to many animals. A rural habitat is also home to a variety of animals. Birds like pigeons and starlings nest on tall buildings. Mice and rats build their nests in or near buildings. Squirrels, rabbits, and opossums make their homes in the wide-open spaces of city parks. Timid animals like foxes and raccoons search for food in neighborhood garbage cans at night. Perhaps the favorite city animals, though, are the ones that live in the homes of people—cats, dogs, and other animal friends we call pets.

6. What is the main idea of this paragraph?

- (F) People should protect city animals.
- (G) Urban animals cause many problems.
- (H) Many animals live in the city.
- (J) People who live in cities should not have pets.

7. What is the author's purpose for writing this paragraph?

- (A) to inform people about animals that live in urban habitats
- (B) to warn people about urban animals
- (C) to persuade city officials about the need to protect animals
- (D) to entertain people with stories about urban animals

GO

8. **Which sentence does not belong in this paragraph?**

   (F) Birds like pigeons and starlings nest on tall buildings.

   (G) An urban habitat is home to many animals.

   (H) A rural habitat is also home to a variety of animals.

   (J) Mice and rats build their nests in or near buildings.

9. **If the author wanted to continue describing urban habitats, what could be a good topic for the next paragraph?**

   (A) career opportunities in cities

   (B) urban crime

   (C) city schools

   (D) plants that can be found in cities

DIRECTIONS: Choose the word that fits in both sentences.

10. **Set the package _____ to the side.**
    We had the day _____ .

    (F) over

    (G) off

    (H) apart

    (J) away

11. **Barb put a clean _____ on the bed.**
    Jason washed the cookie _____ after he finished baking.

    (A) pillow

    (B) tray

    (C) sheet

    (D) cover

DIRECTIONS: Choose the best answer.

12. **Which word means the opposite of the underlined word?**

    <u>ignore</u> the noise

    (F) contribute to

    (G) notice

    (H) overlook

    (J) behave

13. **Which answer means the same as the underlined parts of the words?**

    <u>dis</u>trust   <u>dis</u>honest

    (A) with

    (B) not

    (C) again

    (D) remove

14. **Kim is about to begin reading a book titled *Let Liberty Ring.* Where in the book should Kim look to find out where the book was published?**

    (F) the table of contents

    (G) the copyright page

    (H) the introduction

    (J) the index

15. **Which of these references would provide another word for *beautiful*?**

    (A) encyclopedia

    (B) bibliography

    (C) thesaurus

    (D) almanac

16. **Which of these words has the same *i* sound as the *i* in *light*?**

    (F) dip

    (G) file

    (H) mistake

    (J) puppies

GO

DIRECTIONS: Use the table of contents below to answer questions 17–18.

17. Which of these topics would most likely be found in chapter 3?

- (A) jet engines
- (B) hay fever
- (C) hurricanes
- (D) lips

18. In which chapter would you probably find information about the liver's function?

- (F) chapter 1
- (G) chapter 2
- (H) chapter 3
- (J) chapter 4

DIRECTIONS: Read the passage and then answer questions 19–21.

(1) Imagine going to a college where you can major in video games! (2) Well, all the students at DigiPen School are doing exactly that. (3) A man named Claude Comair founded the college in Vancouver, British Columbia. (4) It has a goal that is to teach students to create computer animation and to also program video games. (5) While this may sound like fun, the school's curriculum is serious business. (6) The teachers are professional programmers and engineers. (7) The classes are taught year-round for two years of intense study. (8) Students typically from 8 A.M. to 9 P.M. Monday through Friday and for much of the day on Saturday.

19. Which sentence could be added after sentence 6?

- (A) Each game requires several programmers, artists, musicians, and designers to make it marketable.
- (B) The classes include advanced mathematics and physics, computer languages, and art.
- (C) The video game industry earns billions of dollars each year.
- (D) The graduates of DigiPen will tell you that they make a living doing what they love best—playing video games.

20. How is sentence 4 best written?

- (F) Its goal is to teach students to create computer animation and video games.
- (G) For its goal, it aims to teach students to create computer animation and program video games.
- (H) Creating computer animation and programming video games is the goal the school sets for all of its students.
- (J) Teaching creating computer animation and programming video games is its goal.

21. Which sentence is incomplete?

- (A) sentence 2
- (B) sentence 4
- (C) sentence 6
- (D) sentence 8

GO

Name _____ Date _____

(1) Gregory's <u>father</u> worked for the Wildlife Department. (2) One day, <u>he</u> came to Gregory's class carrying a small cage. (3) When he <u>opened</u> the top of the cage, a raccoon popped out. (4) The <u>furry</u> little creature walked around the teacher's desk. (5) Everyone <u>really</u> enjoyed watching the raccoon.

22. sentence 1
- Ⓕ noun
- Ⓖ pronoun
- Ⓗ verb
- Ⓙ adjective

23. sentence 2
- Ⓐ noun
- Ⓑ pronoun
- Ⓒ preposition
- Ⓓ conjunction

24. sentence 3
- Ⓕ noun
- Ⓖ pronoun
- Ⓗ verb
- Ⓙ adverb

25. sentence 4
- Ⓐ noun
- Ⓑ verb
- Ⓒ adverb
- Ⓓ adjective

26. sentence 5
- Ⓕ noun
- Ⓖ preposition
- Ⓗ adverb
- Ⓙ adjective

DIRECTIONS: Choose the underlined word that is spelled incorrectly. If all the underlined words are spelled correctly, choose "all correct."

27.
- Ⓐ <u>believe</u> in yourself
- Ⓑ <u>captan</u> of the team
- Ⓒ run an <u>errand</u>
- Ⓓ all correct

28.
- Ⓕ be <u>pateint</u>
- Ⓖ <u>brightly</u> colored
- Ⓗ was <u>frightened</u>
- Ⓙ all correct

DIRECTIONS: Decide which punctuation mark is needed in each sentence.

29. "This is fun, answered Lettie.
- Ⓐ ,
- Ⓑ ?
- Ⓒ "
- Ⓓ '

30. Jeff will you please bring in the newspaper?
- Ⓕ ,
- Ⓖ !
- Ⓗ "
- Ⓙ '

31. Youre early today.
- Ⓐ ,
- Ⓑ ?
- Ⓒ "
- Ⓓ '

GO →

Name _____ Date _____

DIRECTIONS: For numbers 32–35, indicate the correct sentence type.

32. Describe the main characters.

- (F) declarative
- (G) imperative
- (H) interrogative
- (J) exclamatory

33. Will you come back and tell us the story?

- (A) declarative
- (B) imperative
- (C) interrogative
- (D) exclamatory

34. Larry completed his paper route after he left school.

- (F) simple
- (G) compound
- (H) complex
- (J) fragment

35. The bell rang, and the students returned to class.

- (A) simple
- (B) compound
- (C) complex
- (D) fragment

DIRECTIONS: For numbers 36–37, choose the answer that best combines the sentences.

36. Mark will create a collage.
Mark will use photographs for his collage.

- (F) Mark will create a collage, but he will use photographs.
- (G) Mark will use photographs and he will create a collage.
- (H) Mark will create a collage and he will use photographs.
- (J) Mark will create a collage using photographs.

37. Amanda took us to the pond.
She showed us where to find the ducks on the pond.

- (A) Amanda showed us where to find the ducks on the pond that she took us to.
- (B) Amanda took us to the pond and showed us where to find the ducks.
- (C) Amanda took us to find the ducks, and also where to find the pond.
- (D) Amanda showed us where to find the pond and where to find the ducks.

STOP

Final English/Language Arts Test
Answer Sheet

1	Ⓐ Ⓑ Ⓒ Ⓓ		21	Ⓐ Ⓑ Ⓒ Ⓓ
2	Ⓕ Ⓖ Ⓗ Ⓙ		22	Ⓕ Ⓖ Ⓗ Ⓙ
3	Ⓐ Ⓑ Ⓒ Ⓓ		23	Ⓐ Ⓑ Ⓒ Ⓓ
4	Ⓕ Ⓖ Ⓗ Ⓙ		24	Ⓕ Ⓖ Ⓗ Ⓙ
5	Ⓐ Ⓑ Ⓒ Ⓓ		25	Ⓐ Ⓑ Ⓒ Ⓓ
6	Ⓕ Ⓖ Ⓗ Ⓙ		26	Ⓕ Ⓖ Ⓗ Ⓙ
7	Ⓐ Ⓑ Ⓒ Ⓓ		27	Ⓐ Ⓑ Ⓒ Ⓓ
8	Ⓕ Ⓖ Ⓗ Ⓙ		28	Ⓕ Ⓖ Ⓗ Ⓙ
9	Ⓐ Ⓑ Ⓒ Ⓓ		29	Ⓐ Ⓑ Ⓒ Ⓓ
10	Ⓕ Ⓖ Ⓗ Ⓙ		30	Ⓕ Ⓖ Ⓗ Ⓙ
11	Ⓐ Ⓑ Ⓒ Ⓓ		31	Ⓐ Ⓑ Ⓒ Ⓓ
12	Ⓕ Ⓖ Ⓗ Ⓙ		32	Ⓕ Ⓖ Ⓗ Ⓙ
13	Ⓐ Ⓑ Ⓒ Ⓓ		33	Ⓐ Ⓑ Ⓒ Ⓓ
14	Ⓕ Ⓖ Ⓗ Ⓙ		34	Ⓕ Ⓖ Ⓗ Ⓙ
15	Ⓐ Ⓑ Ⓒ Ⓓ		35	Ⓐ Ⓑ Ⓒ Ⓓ
16	Ⓕ Ⓖ Ⓗ Ⓙ		36	Ⓕ Ⓖ Ⓗ Ⓙ
17	Ⓐ Ⓑ Ⓒ Ⓓ		37	Ⓐ Ⓑ Ⓒ Ⓓ
18	Ⓕ Ⓖ Ⓗ Ⓙ			
19	Ⓐ Ⓑ Ⓒ Ⓓ			
20	Ⓕ Ⓖ Ⓗ Ⓙ			

Georgia Mathematics
Content Standards

The mathematics section measures knowledge in six different areas:

1) **Number and Operations**

2) **Measurement**

3) **Geometry**

4) **Algebra**

5) **Data Analysis**

6) **Process Skills**

Georgia Mathematics
Table of Contents

Number and Operations Standards

M5N. Number and Operations

Students will further develop their understanding of the concept of whole numbers. They will also understand the meanings of multiplication and division of decimal fractions and use decimal fractions and common fractions in computation, as well as in problem-solving situations.

M5N1. Students will further develop their understanding of whole numbers. *(See pages 82–83.)*

a. Classify the set of counting numbers into subsets with distinguishing characteristics (odd/even, prime/composite).
b. Find multiples and factors.
c. Analyze and use divisibility rules.

What it means:

- A **prime number** is a whole number that has only two factors, 1 and itself. Examples of prime numbers are 1, 3, 11, 13, and 17.
- A **composite number** is a whole number that has more than two factors. For example, 12 is a composite number because 1, 2, 3, 4, 6, and 12 are its factors.
- A **factor** is a number that divides evenly into another number. For example, the numbers 1, 3, 5, and 15 are all factors of 15.
- A **multiple** is the result of a number multiplied by any whole number. For example, the multiples of 5 are 0, 5, 10, 15, 20, and so on.

M5N2. Students will further develop their understanding of decimal fractions as part of the base-ten number system. *(See page 84.)*

a. Understand place value.
b. Analyze the effect on the product when a number is multiplied by 10, 100, 1000, 0.1, and 0.01.

What it means:

- Students should be able to identify place values on both sides of a decimal point (ones, tens, hundreds, and thousands to the left of the decimal point, and tenths and hundredths to the right of the decimal point).

M5N3. Students will further develop their understanding of the meaning of multiplication and division with decimal fractions and use them. *(See pages 85–86.)*

a. Model multiplication and division of decimal fractions by another decimal fraction.
b. Explain the process of multiplication and division, including situations in which the multiplier and divisor are both whole numbers and decimal fractions.
c. Multiply and divide with decimal fractions including decimal fractions less than one and greater than one.
d. Understand the relationships and rules for multiplication and division of whole numbers also apply to decimal fractions.

Number and Operations Standards

M5N4. Students will continue to develop their understanding of the meaning of common fractions and compute with them. *(See pages 87–90.)*

a. Understand division of whole numbers can be represented as a fraction
   ($a/b = a \div b$).
b. Understand the value of a fraction is not changed when both its numerator and denominator are multiplied or divided by the same number because it is the same as multiplying or dividing by one.
c. Find equivalent fractions and simplify fractions.
d. Model the multiplication and division of common fractions.
e. Explore finding common denominators using concrete, pictorial, and computational models.
f. Use $<$, $>$, or $=$ to compare fractions and justify the comparison.
g. Add and subtract common fractions and mixed numbers with unlike denominators.
h. Use fractions (proper and improper) and decimal fractions interchangeably.
i. Estimate products and quotients.

What it means:

● A proper fraction is one in which the numerator is less than the denominator (e.g., $\frac{1}{2}$).

● An improper fraction is one in which the numerator is larger than or equal to the denominator (e.g., $\frac{5}{3}$).

M5N5. Students will understand the meaning of percentage. *(See page 91.)*

a. Model percent on 10-by-10 grids.
b. Apply percentage to circle graphs.

Mathematics

M5N1

Primes, Composites, Factors, and Multiples

DIRECTIONS: Choose the best answer.

Clue   **Primes** are whole numbers that have only two factors, 1 and itself. **Composites** are numbers that have more than two factors. A **factor** is a number that divides evenly into another number. A **multiple** is the result of a number multiplied by any whole number.

1. Which number is a prime number?
   - (A) 20
   - (B) 15
   - (C) 10
   - (D) 5

2. Which number is a composite number?
   - (F) 4
   - (G) 5
   - (H) 11
   - (J) 17

3. For which of the following is the answer a prime number?
   - (A) 3×4
   - (B) $15 - 5$
   - (C) 2×2
   - (D) $9 \div 3$

4. For which of the following is the answer a composite number?
   - (F) 3×1
   - (G) 2×0
   - (H) $7 + 4$
   - (J) $8 + 16$

5. How would you write 36 as the product of its prime factors?
   - (A) 6×6
   - (B) 3×12
   - (C) $2 \times 2 \times 3 \times 3$
   - (D) 4×9

6. How would you write 40 as the product of its prime factors?
   - (F) 2×20
   - (G) $2 \times 2 \times 2 \times 5$
   - (H) 8×5
   - (J) 4×10

7. Which number is a multiple of 9?
   - (A) 18
   - (B) 20
   - (C) 38
   - (D) 50

8. Which number is a multiple of both 5 and 6?
   - (F) 10
   - (G) 12
   - (H) 15
   - (J) 30

STOP

Georgia Test Practice

Mathematics

M5N1

Divisibility Rules

Number and
Operations

DIRECTIONS: Choose the best answer.

> **Divisible by 2:** Any number with a final digit of 0 or an even number.
> For example: 45,65<u>2</u>, when divided by 2, divides evenly to 22,826.
>
> **Divisible by 3:** Any number with the sum of all the digits being divisible by 3.
> For example: 977,355 ÷ 3 = 325,785 (9 + 7 + 7 + 3 + 5 + 5 = 36 and
> 36 ÷ 3 = 12).
>
> **Divisible by 5:** Any number with a last digit of 0 or 5.
> For example: 1,253,45<u>5</u> ÷ 5 = 250,691.
>
> **Divisible by 10:** Any number with a last digit of 0.
> For example: 456,890 ÷ 10 = 45,689.

1. **Which number is divisible by 5?**

   (A) 321

   (B) 333

   (C) 250

   (D) 364

2. **Which number is divisible by 2 and 3?**

   (F) 104,924

   (G) 27

   (H) 5,401

   (J) 444

3. **The number 156,945 is divisible by which of the following?**

   (A) 5 and 10

   (B) 5 only

   (C) 2 and 3

   (D) 10 only

4. **The number 250 is divisible by which of the following?**

   (F) 2, 5, and 10

   (G) 5 and 10

   (H) 2, 3, and 5

   (J) 2, 3, 5, and 10

5. **The sum of 27,185 and 27,001 is divisible by which numbers?**

   (A) 2, 3, and 5

   (B) 2 only

   (C) 5 only

   (D) 2 and 3

6. **The difference between 565 and 455 is divisible by which numbers?**

   (F) 2 and 5

   (G) 5 and 10

   (H) 2, 5, and 10

   (J) 3 and 10

STOP

Mathematics

M5N2

Understanding Place Value
of Decimal Fractions

DIRECTIONS: Choose the best answer.

1. **In which numeral is there a 5 in both the tens and the thousandths place?**
   - (A) 3,451.563
   - (B) 3,541.563
   - (C) 3,451.635
   - (D) 5,341.653

2. **Which of these decimals is the largest?**
   - (F) 9.561
   - (G) 9.631
   - (H) 9.546
   - (J) 9.547

3. **Which of these has a 4 in the hundredths place?**
   - (A) 4.523
   - (B) 8.634
   - (C) 3.844
   - (D) 7.498

4. **What is the value of the 2 in 9,180,673.24?**
   - (F) 2 millions
   - (G) 2 hundred thousands
   - (H) 2 thousands
   - (J) 2 tenths

5. **Which group of decimals is ordered from least to greatest?**
   - (A) 4.482, 4.483, 4.481, 4.408
   - (B) 4.576, 4.432, 4.678, 4.104
   - (C) 4.978, 4.652, 4.331, 4.320
   - (D) 4.269, 4.692, 4.699, 4.732

6. **What is the value of 6 in 89.634?**
   - (F) 6 tens
   - (G) 6 hundreds
   - (H) 6 tenths
   - (J) 6 hundredths

7. **If 6.32 is multiplied by 100, the product is _____ .**
   - (A) 63.2
   - (B) 6.3200
   - (C) 6,320
   - (D) 632

8. **If 4,593 is multiplied by 0.01, the product is _____ .**
   - (F) 459.3
   - (G) 45.93
   - (H) 4.593
   - (J) 45,930

STOP

84

Mathematics

M5N3

Multiplying and Dividing Decimal Fractions

DIRECTIONS: Choose the best answer.

 Clue To determine the decimal point in the product (the answer for a multiplication problem), count the number of decimal places in the factors.

1. 3.6
    × 6

  (A) 2.16
  (B) 216
  (C) 21.6
  (D) none of these

2. 0.13 × 4 =

  (F) 0.52
  (G) 0.50
  (H) 0.59
  (J) none of these

3. 6.87 × 4 =

  (A) 27.48
  (B) 2.748
  (C) 274.8
  (D) none of these

4. 2.03
    × 0.02

  (F) 0.406
  (G) 0.0406
  (H) 2.006
  (J) none of these

5. 3)7.2

  (A) 2.4
  (B) 2.12
  (C) 2.89
  (D) none of these

6. 0.12 × 6 =

  (F) 0.84
  (G) 0.96
  (H) 0.72
  (J) none of these

7. 0.32 × 2 =

  (A) 0.36
  (B) 0.70
  (C) 0.66
  (D) none of these

8. 0.37 ÷ 5 =

  (F) 0.086
  (G) 0.074
  (H) 0.065
  (J) none of these

9. 11.13 ÷ 5.3 =

  (A) 5.83
  (B) 16.43
  (C) 2.10
  (D) none of these

10. 28.86 ÷ 3.9 =

  (F) 112.554
  (G) 7.4
  (H) 24.96
  (J) none of these

STOP

Mathematics

M5N3

Number and
Operations

Using
Decimal Fractions

DIRECTIONS: Choose the best answer.

1. Triplets Brad, Chad, and Tad received a birthday card from their grandmother. She included a check for $45.75 and told them that each of them should get the same amount after the check is cashed. How much will each boy get if they divide the check equally?

    (A) $15.00

    (B) $15.15

    (C) $15.25

    (D) $15.50

2. Keisha and Darlene split a pizza. The pizza cost $18.98. If they both chipped in the same amount to pay for the pizza, how much did each one contribute?

    (F) $9.49

    (G) $9.50

    (H) $8.49

    (J) $8.50

3. Randy bought five boxes of his favorite cereal—Sugar Spazzers—at the grocery store. The total cost of the five boxes was $18.65. How much does one box of Sugar Spazzers cost?

    (A) $5.73

    (B) $4.72

    (C) $3.93

    (D) $3.73

4. Isaiah bought 2.5 gallons of gasoline for his lawn mower. He paid $4.95 for the 2.5 gallons. How much would one gallon of gasoline have cost him?

    (F) $1.98

    (G) $1.58

    (H) $2.63

    (J) $1.95

5. Jamie made $12.75 for three hours of babysitting last Saturday evening. How much was she paid per hour?

    (A) $3.75

    (B) $4.00

    (C) $4.25

    (D) $4.55

6. The total purchase price of Barbara's DVD player was $180.65. If she makes five equal payments to the store to buy the DVD player, what will be the amount of each payment?

    (F) $30.11

    (G) $36.13

    (H) $60.22

    (J) $66.13

STOP

Georgia Test Practice

Mathematics

M5N4

Finding Equivalent Fractions

DIRECTIONS: Choose the best answer.

1. Which of the following is *not* equivalent to $\frac{3}{4}$?

   Ⓐ $\frac{34}{100}$

   Ⓑ $\frac{9}{12}$

   Ⓒ $\frac{15}{20}$

   Ⓓ $\frac{75}{100}$

2. The puzzle had 100 pieces. Eight of the pieces were solid white. Which fraction does *not* show how many of the pieces were solid white?

   Ⓕ $\frac{8}{100}$

   Ⓖ $\frac{4}{50}$

   Ⓗ $\frac{2}{25}$

   Ⓙ $\frac{1}{10}$

3. Which of the following is *not* equivalent to $\frac{1}{2}$?

   Ⓐ $\frac{50}{100}$

   Ⓑ $\frac{2}{10}$

   Ⓒ $\frac{2}{4}$

   Ⓓ $\frac{5}{10}$

4. Which of the following is equivalent to $\frac{3}{10}$?

   Ⓕ $\frac{1}{3}$

   Ⓖ $\frac{2}{9}$

   Ⓗ $\frac{6}{20}$

   Ⓙ none of these

5. This fraction picture shows that $\frac{1}{2}$ means the same as which other fraction?

   Ⓐ $\frac{1}{4}$

   Ⓑ $\frac{1}{8}$

   Ⓒ $\frac{2}{8}$

   Ⓓ $\frac{4}{8}$

   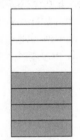

6. Which figure is less than $\frac{3}{4}$ shaded?

   Ⓕ

   Ⓖ

   Ⓗ

   Ⓙ

STOP

Mathematics

M5N4

Multiplying and Dividing Fractions

DIRECTIONS: Multiply the fractions to complete this table.

×	$\frac{3}{5}$	$\frac{1}{2}$	$\frac{2}{3}$	$\frac{1}{6}$	$\frac{8}{8}$
$\frac{1}{2}$	$\frac{3}{10}$				
$\frac{3}{8}$					
$\frac{4}{7}$					
$\frac{5}{8}$					
$\frac{1}{10}$					

DIRECTIONS: Work the problems. Show your work like this:

$$6 \div \frac{1}{4} = \frac{6}{1} \div \frac{1}{4} = \frac{6}{1} \times \frac{4}{1} = \frac{24}{1} = 24$$

1. $7 \div \frac{1}{3} =$	5. $8 \div \frac{1}{2} =$
2. $16 \div \frac{1}{3} =$	6. $2\frac{1}{2} \div \frac{1}{2} =$
3. $6 \div \frac{1}{2} =$	7. $18 \div \frac{1}{7} =$
4. $3\frac{1}{9} \div \frac{1}{3} =$	8. $5\frac{1}{4} \div \frac{3}{8} =$

STOP

Georgia Test Practice

Mathematics

M5N4

Adding and Subtracting Fractions

DIRECTIONS: Solve the problems. Reduce answers to lowest terms or write as mixed numbers.

1.
$$\begin{array}{r} \frac{1}{10} \\ + \frac{4}{5} \\ \hline \end{array}$$

2.
$$\begin{array}{r} \frac{3}{4} \\ + \frac{1}{5} \\ \hline \end{array}$$

3.
$$\begin{array}{r} \frac{1}{5} \\ + \frac{1}{3} \\ \hline \end{array}$$

4.
$$\begin{array}{r} 16\frac{2}{7} \\ +14\frac{1}{3} \\ \hline \end{array}$$

5.
$$\begin{array}{r} 40\frac{1}{2} \\ +50\frac{2}{3} \\ \hline \end{array}$$

6.
$$\begin{array}{r} 84\frac{5}{6} \\ +94\frac{2}{3} \\ \hline \end{array}$$

7.
$$\begin{array}{r} \frac{1}{3} \\ - \frac{1}{4} \\ \hline \end{array}$$

8.
$$\begin{array}{r} \frac{2}{3} \\ - \frac{2}{5} \\ \hline \end{array}$$

9.
$$\begin{array}{r} \frac{5}{9} \\ - \frac{1}{2} \\ \hline \end{array}$$

10.
$$\begin{array}{r} 3\frac{4}{7} \\ - 1\frac{1}{14} \\ \hline \end{array}$$

11.
$$\begin{array}{r} 8\frac{5}{6} \\ - 3\frac{3}{8} \\ \hline \end{array}$$

12.
$$\begin{array}{r} 7\frac{7}{8} \\ - 2\frac{1}{4} \\ \hline \end{array}$$

STOP

Mathematics

M5N4

Comparing Decimals and Fractions

DIRECTIONS: For each problem, write the symbol < *(less than)*, > *(greater than)*, or = *(equivalent to)* to make the expression true.

Examples:

1.3 is $> 1\frac{1}{4}$

$\frac{3}{4}$ is $= 0.75$

$\frac{5}{6}$ is < 0.85

1. $\frac{1}{2}$ _____ 0.6

2. $\frac{5}{4}$ _____ 1.1

3. $\frac{2}{3}$ _____ $\frac{6}{9}$

4. $\frac{7}{8}$ _____ 0.9

5. $\frac{4}{5}$ _____ 0.5

6. $\frac{1}{5}$ _____ 0.2

7. $1\frac{1}{2}$ _____ 1.7

8. $\frac{9}{13}$ _____ $\frac{9}{10}$

9. 1.25 _____ $1\frac{1}{4}$

10. 0.5 _____ $\frac{3}{6}$

11. 0.25 _____ $\frac{2}{5}$

12. $\frac{5}{3}$ _____ $2\frac{1}{3}$

13. 0.4 _____ $\frac{4}{8}$

14. 1.8 _____ $\frac{1}{8}$

15. 0.3 _____ $\frac{2}{6}$

16. 0.1 _____ $\frac{2}{20}$

17. 0.7 _____ $\frac{7}{8}$

18. $\frac{6}{9}$ _____ $\frac{1}{3}$

19. $\frac{5}{8}$ _____ $\frac{1}{2}$

20. 0.75 _____ $\frac{8}{10}$

Mathematics

M5N5

Modeling Percentages

DIRECTIONS: For each problem, choose the percentage that represents the shaded part of the figure.

1.
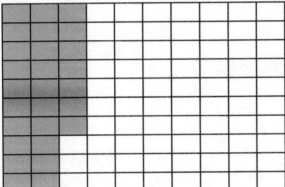

Ⓐ 23%

Ⓑ 27%

Ⓒ 49%

Ⓓ 72%

2.
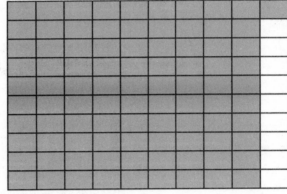

Ⓕ 9%

Ⓖ 9.1%

Ⓗ 90%

Ⓙ 91%

DIRECTIONS: Show the information below in a circle graph. Then answer the question about the graph.

Circle graphs are often used to show percentages. Below are the results from a survey about students' favorite school subjects.

Subject	Percentage
English	20%
Math	10%
Science	10%
Social Studies	10%
Computers	20%
Music	30%

3. **Favorite School Subjects**

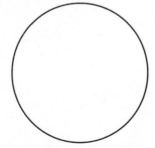

4. **What are the greatest and least values in this circle graph?**

_____

_____

_____

Mathematics

M5N1–M5N5

For pages 82–91

Mini-Test 1

DIRECTIONS: Choose the best answer.

1. What is the value of 6 in 89.634?

Ⓐ 6 tens

Ⓑ 6 hundreds

Ⓒ 6 tenths

Ⓓ 6 hundredths

2. $2\frac{33}{100}$

Ⓕ 23.3

Ⓖ 0.233

Ⓗ 233

Ⓙ 2.33

3. Which of these is a prime number?

Ⓐ 19

Ⓑ 21

Ⓒ 32

Ⓓ 48

4. What are all of the factors of the product 5 × 4?

Ⓕ 2, 4, 5, and 10

Ⓖ 1, 2, 4, 5, 10, and 20

Ⓗ 1, 4, 5, and 9

Ⓙ 1, 2, 3, 4, 5, 6, 10, and 20

5. What is the decimal equivalent of $\frac{5}{8}$?

Ⓐ 0.58

Ⓑ 0.625

Ⓒ 1.6

Ⓓ 0.6

6. Which of these is another way to write $\frac{7}{11}$?

Ⓕ $\frac{21}{35}$

Ⓖ $\frac{35}{66}$

Ⓗ $\frac{28}{44}$

Ⓙ $\frac{11}{15}$

7. Which number shows the value of the shaded portion of this figure?

Ⓐ $\frac{2}{5}$

Ⓑ 60%

Ⓒ 0.5

Ⓓ 2.1

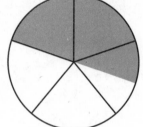

8. $7\frac{1}{4} - 5\frac{1}{5}$

Ⓕ $1\frac{2}{5}$

Ⓖ $2\frac{1}{20}$

Ⓗ $1\frac{19}{20}$

Ⓙ none of these

9. 0.33 × 2.4 =

Ⓐ 0.792

Ⓑ 0.927

Ⓒ 0.872

Ⓓ none of these

STOP

Georgia Test Practice

Measurement Standards

M5M. Measurement

Students will compute the area of geometric plane figures. They will also understand the concept of volume and compute the volume of simple geometric solids and measure capacity. Students will convert from one unit to another within one system of measurement.

M5M1. Students will extend their understanding of area of fundamental geometric plane figures. *(See pages 94–97.)*

a. Estimate the area of fundamental geometric plane figures.
b. Derive the formula for the area of a parallelogram (e.g., cut the parallelogram apart and rearrange it into a rectangle of the same area).
c. Derive the formula for the area of a triangle (e.g., demonstrate and explain its relationship to the area of a rectangle with the same base and height).
d. Find the areas of triangles and parallelograms using formulae.
e. Estimate the area of a circle through partitioning and tiling and then with formula (let $\pi = 3.14$). (Discuss square units as they apply to circles.)
f. Find the area of a polygon (regular and irregular) by dividing it into squares, rectangles, and/or triangles and find the sum of the areas of those shapes.

What it means:
- **Area** is the amount of space inside a two-dimensional figure.

M5M3. Students will measure capacity with appropriately chosen units and tools. *(See page 98.)*

a. Use milliliters, liters, fluid ounces, cups, pints, quarts, and gallons to measure capacity.
b. Compare one unit to another within a single system of measurement (e.g., 1 quart = 2 pints).

M5M4. Students will understand and compute the volume of a simple geometric solid. *(See pages 99–100.)*

a. Understand a cubic unit (u^3) is represented by a cube in which each edge has the length of 1 unit.
b. Identify the units used in computing volume as cubic centimeters (cm^3), cubic meters (m^3), cubic inches (in.^{3}), cubic feet (ft.^{3}), and cubic yards (yd.^{3}).
c. Derive the formula for finding the volume of a cube and a rectangular prism using manipulatives.
d. Compute the volume of a cube and a rectangular prism using formulae.
e. Estimate the volume of a simple geometric solid.
f. Understand the similarities and differences between volume and capacity.

What it means:
- **Volume** is the amount of space inside a three-dimensional figure.

Mathematics   **Measurement**

Estimating Area

DIRECTIONS: Estimate the *area* of each shape by counting the square units.

Clue   **Area** is the amount of space contained in a surface.

1.
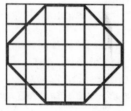
_____

2.
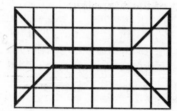
_____

3.
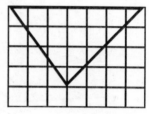
_____

4.
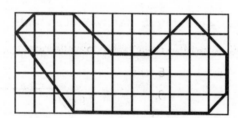
_____

5.
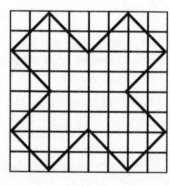
_____

6.
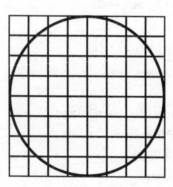
_____

7.
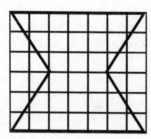
_____

8.
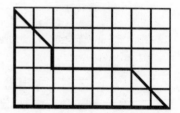
_____

STOP

Name _____   Date _____

Mathematics   Measurement

M5M1   # Finding the Area of Triangles
                and Parallelograms

DIRECTIONS: Choose the best answer.

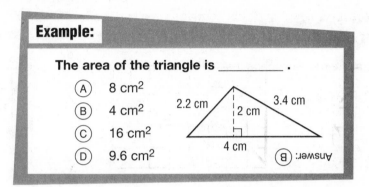

Example:

The area of the triangle is _____ .

- (A) 8 cm²
- (B) 4 cm²
- (C) 16 cm²
- (D) 9.6 cm²

2.2 cm   2 cm   3.4 cm

4 cm

Answer: (B)

1. The area of a parallelogram is equal to _____ .

- (A) twice the area of the triangle with the same base and height
- (B) the area of the rectangle with the same side lengths
- (C) twice the area of the rectangle with the same side lengths
- (D) the area of the square with the same base

2. The area of a parallelogram with base = 4 cm and height = 2 cm is _____ .

- (F) 8 cm²
- (G) 4 cm²
- (H) 16 cm²
- (J) 32 cm²

3. Two of the same triangles make a parallelogram with _____ .

- (A) three fourths the area
- (B) half the area
- (C) the same area
- (D) twice the area

4. Find the area of the triangle.

- (F) 8.5 yd.²
- (G) 3 yd.²
- (H) 2.7 yd.²
- (J) 6 yd.²

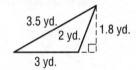

3.5 yd.   2 yd.   1.8 yd.

3 yd.

5. Find the area of the parallelogram.

- (A) 5.1 m²
- (B) 6.46 m²
- (C) 2.55 m²
- (D) 6.8 m²

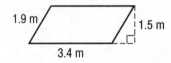

1.9 m   1.5 m

3.4 m

6. Find the area of a triangle with base = 5 and height = 3.

- (F) 7.5 square units
- (G) 8 square units
- (H) 15 square units
- (J) 4 square units

7. Find the area of a parallelogram with base = 5 and height = 3.

- (A) 7.5 units²
- (B) 8 units²
- (C) 15 units²
- (D) 4 units²

STOP

Mathematics

M5M1

Measurement

Finding the
Area of Circles

DIRECTIONS: Find the area of each circle below. Include the appropriate units in your answer.

Example:

The **area** of a circle is the space inside the circle.

$A = \pi r^2$, where r = radius

$\pi = 3.14$

$A = \pi r^2 = 3.14 \times 14^2 = 3.14 \times 196 = 615.44$ cm²

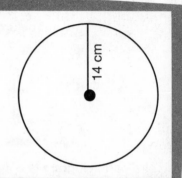

1. _____

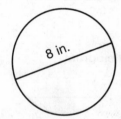
8 in.

2. _____

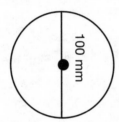
100 mm

3. _____

3 in.

4. _____

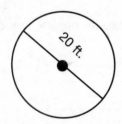
20 ft.

5. _____

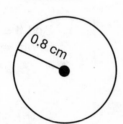
0.8 cm

6. _____

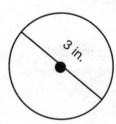
$\frac{1}{2}$ mm

7. _____

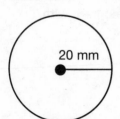
20 mm

8. _____

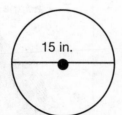
15 in.

9. _____

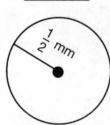
2.1 m

STOP

M5M1

Finding the Area of Irregular Polygons

DIRECTIONS: Find the area of each shape. Include the correct units in your answer.

Example:

Irregular spaces can be divided into common shapes, such as rectangles and right triangles, as shown in the diagram below. If you find the area of each small shape using rules, you can add their areas together to find the area of the large shape.

Region 1 = $\frac{1}{2} bh = \frac{1}{2} \times 2 \times 2.5 = 2.5$ m²

Region 2 = $bh = 3 \times 2.5 = 7.5$ m²

Region 3 = $bh = 1.5 \times 1.7 = 2.55$ m²

+ Region 4 = $\frac{1}{2} bh = \frac{1}{2} \times 1 \times 1.7 = 0.85$ m²

_____

Total Area = 13.4 m²

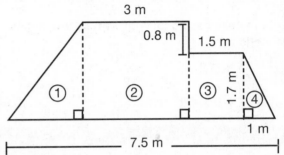

1.

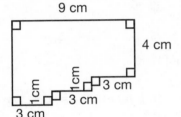

Area: _____

2.

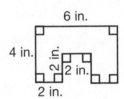

Area: _____

3.

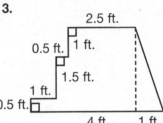

Area: _____

4.

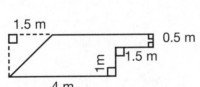

Area: _____

5.

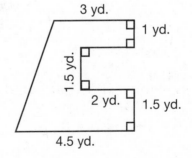

Area: _____

STOP

Mathematics

M5M3

Measuring Capacity

DIRECTIONS: Choose the best answer.

Clue

Use these conversions to help you figure out the correct measurements.
1 gallon (gal.) = 4 quarts (qt.)
1 quart (qt.) = 2 pints (pt.)
1 pint (pt.) = 2 cups (c.)
1 cup (c.) = 8 fluid ounces (fl. oz.)

1. A recipe calls for 6 quarts of water. How many gallons is that?

   Ⓐ 1 gallon

   Ⓑ $1\frac{1}{2}$ gallons

   Ⓒ 2 gallons

   Ⓓ $2\frac{1}{2}$ gallons

2. Another recipe calls for 5 cups of milk. How many pints is that?

   Ⓕ $2\frac{1}{2}$ pints

   Ⓖ $1\frac{1}{4}$ pints

   Ⓗ $2\frac{1}{4}$ pints

   Ⓙ $1\frac{1}{2}$ pints

3. 1 liter = _____

   Ⓐ 10 milliliters

   Ⓑ 100 milliliters

   Ⓒ 1000 milliliters

   Ⓓ 0.1 milliliter

4. 4 gallons = _____

   Ⓕ 40 cups

   Ⓖ 8 quarts

   Ⓗ 16 pints

   Ⓙ 64 cups

5. 16 cups is equivalent to all of the following except _____ .

   Ⓐ 8 pints

   Ⓑ 1 gallon

   Ⓒ 4 quarts

   Ⓓ 100 fluid ounces

6. 4 quarts + 2 pints = _____

   Ⓕ 1 gallon + 1 quart

   Ⓖ $1\frac{1}{2}$ gallons

   Ⓗ 10 cups

   Ⓙ 20 pints

7. A broken pipe in a factory is leaking water at the rate of 2 pints per hour. It leaks for 2 days before it can be repaired. How many gallons of water were lost because of the leak?

   Ⓐ 96 gallons

   Ⓑ 12 gallons

   Ⓒ 4 gallons

   Ⓓ 24 gallons

8. Which of the following can hold the greatest amount of liquid?

   Ⓕ a one-gallon jug

   Ⓖ a one-pint measuring cup

   Ⓗ a one-quart bucket

   Ⓙ a one-liter bottle

STOP

Mathematics

M5M4

Understanding Volume

DIRECTIONS: Find the *volume* of each space figure by counting the cubes.

Clue   **Volume** is the measure of the inside of a space figure.

1.
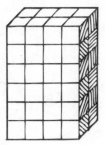

_____

2.
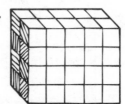

_____

3.
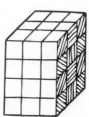

_____

4.
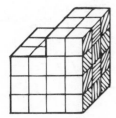

_____

5.
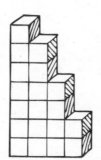

_____

6.
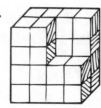

_____

7.
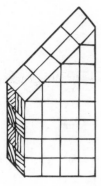

_____

8.
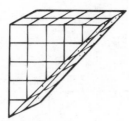

_____

9.
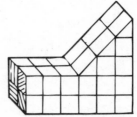

_____

M5M4

Computing the Volume of Rectangular Prisms

DIRECTIONS: Find the volume of the following rectangular prisms. Include the appropriate units in your answer.

Volume of a prism = area of base × height

The base of a rectangular prism is a rectangle.

Area of a rectangle = length × width

Volume of a rectangular prism
= length × width x height

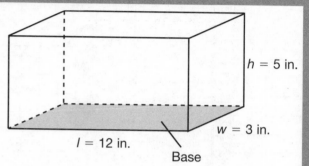

$V = lwh$
$V = 12$ in. $\times 3$ in. $\times 5$ in. $= 36 \times 5 = 180$ in.^{3}

1.

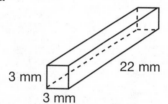

5 in.
4 in.
9 in.

Volume: _____

2.

22 mm
3 mm
3 mm

Volume: _____

3.

4 cm
4 cm
5 cm

Volume: _____

4.

6 m
6 m
6 m

Volume: _____

5.

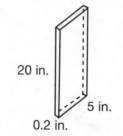

20 in.
5 in.
0.2 in.

Volume: _____

6.

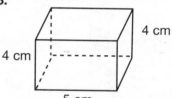

1 ft.
3 ft.
6 ft.

Volume: _____

7.

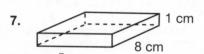

1 cm
8 cm
5 cm

Volume: _____

8.

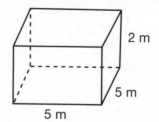

2 m
5 m
5 m

Volume: _____

9.

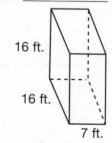

16 ft.
16 ft.
7 ft.

Volume: _____

STOP

Mathematics   **Measurement**

Mini-Test 2

For pages 94–100

DIRECTIONS: Choose the best answer.

1. What is the approximate area of this shape?

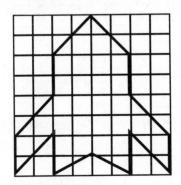

- Ⓐ 24 square units
- Ⓑ 32 square units
- Ⓒ 34 square units
- Ⓓ 38 square units

2. What is the area of this triangle?

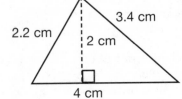

- Ⓕ 8 cm²
- Ⓖ 4 cm²
- Ⓗ 4.4 cm²
- Ⓙ 3.4 cm²

3. What is the area of this circle?

- Ⓐ 31.4 in.²
- Ⓑ 62.8 in.²
- Ⓒ 78.5 in.²
- Ⓓ 314 in.²

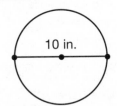

4. Which of the following amounts is largest?

- Ⓕ $\frac{1}{2}$ gallon
- Ⓖ 3 quarts
- Ⓗ 4 pints
- Ⓙ 7 cups

5. 8 gallons + 6 quarts = _____

- Ⓐ 76 pints
- Ⓑ 152 cups
- Ⓒ 38 quarts
- Ⓓ all of the above

6. 200 milliliters = _____

- Ⓕ 2 liters
- Ⓖ 20 liters
- Ⓗ 0.2 liters
- Ⓙ none of these

7. What is the volume of this figure?

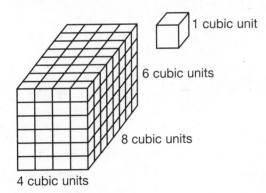

- Ⓐ 18 cubic units
- Ⓑ 192 cubic units
- Ⓒ 32 cubic units
- Ⓓ 48 cubic units

8. What is the volume of this figure?

- Ⓕ 25 m³
- Ⓖ 125 m³
- Ⓗ 15 m³
- Ⓙ 50 m³

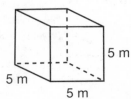

STOP

Geometry, Algebra, and Data Analysis Standards

M5G. Geometry
Students will further develop their understanding of geometric figures.

M5G1. Students will understand congruence of geometric figures and the correspondence of their vertices, sides, and angles. *(See page 103.)*

What it means:
- **Congruent** figures have the same measures of angles and sides.

M5G2. Students will understand the relationship of the circumference of a circle to its diameter is pi ($\pi = 3.14$). *(See page 104.)*

What it means:
- The **circumference** of a circle is the distance around the outside of the circle.

M5A. Algebra
Students will represent and investigate mathematical expressions algebraically by using variables.

What it means:
- A variable is an amount that is not known.

M5A1. Students will represent and interpret the relationships between quantities algebraically. *(See pages 105–106.)*
a. Use variables, such as *n* or *x,* for unknown quantities in algebraic expressions.
b. Investigate simple algebraic expressions by substituting numbers for the unknown.
c. Determine that a formula will be reliable regardless of the type of number (whole numbers or decimal fractions) substituted for the variable.

M5D. Data Analysis
Students will gather, organize, and display data and interpret graphs.

M5D1. Students will analyze graphs. *(See page 107.)*
a. Analyze data presented in a graph.
b. Compare and contrast multiple graphic representations (circle graphs, line graphs, bar graphs, etc.) for a single set of data and discuss the advantages/disadvantages of each.

M5D2. Students will collect, organize, and display data using the most appropriate graph. *(See page 108.)*

Name _____ Date _____

Mathematics

M5G1

Congruence of Geometric Figures

DIRECTIONS: Measure the angles and sides of the shapes. Write *congruent* or *similar* below each set of shapes based on your findings.

Congruent shapes have the same measures of angles and sides.
Similar shapes have the same measures of angles, but not of sides.

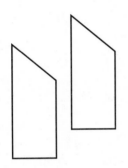

1. _____

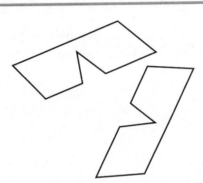

2. _____

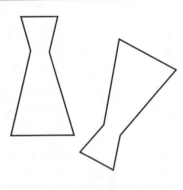

3. _____

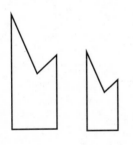

4. _____

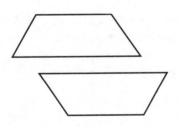

5. _____

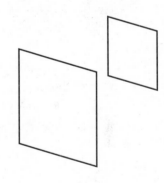

6. _____

7. _____

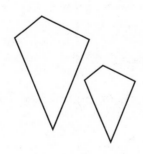

8. _____

9. _____

STOP

Mathematics   Geometry

M5G2   Relationship Between Diameter,
       Radius, and Circumference

DIRECTIONS: Choose the best answer. Use the provided circle for reference as needed.

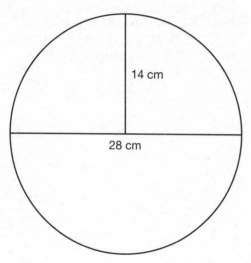

Diameter 28 = cm
Radius 14 = cm
Pi (π) = 3.14
Circumference = 87.92 cm

1. **The circumference of a circle is _____ times its diameter.**

   (A)   2

   (B)   3.14

   (C)   14

   (D)   none of these

2. **The radius of a circle is _____ times its diameter.**

   (F)   14

   (G)   3.14

   (H)   2

   (J)   0.5

3. **Pi (π) represents _____ .**

   (A)   the circumference of a circle divided by its radius

   (B)   the diameter of a circle multiplied by its radius

   (C)   the circumference of a circle divided by its diameter

   (D)   the radius of a circle divided by its diameter

4. **Diameter = _____**

   (F)   2 × radius

   (G)   3.14 × radius

   (H)   Circumference ÷ radius

   (J)   2 × π

5. **Diameter = _____**

   (A)   π × radius

   (B)   Circumference ÷ π

   (C)   Circumference × π

   (D)   none of these

Name _____ Date _____

Using Variables

DIRECTIONS: Choose a variable for the unknown amount. Then write a number sentence to repr[esent the] problem. Finally, draw a model for the equation and find the solution.

Example:

A **variable** is an amount that is not known. It is often represented by a letter. Variables are used in number sentences that represent a situation. A model is a picture of the situation.

Kyle made a dozen cookies. His little sister ate 5 of them.
How many cookies are left?

Variable: Let c = number of cookies left.

Number Sentence: $c + 5 = 12$

Model: a.    b.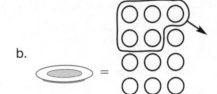

Solution:  $c = 7$

1. **Julie is playing a board game. She rolls a 3 on the first die. What must she roll to move 9 spaces?**

   Number sentence: _____

   Model:

   Solution: _____

2. **Jacob has a bag with 4 pieces of candy. His father puts another handful into the bag. Jacob then has 13 pieces. How many pieces did his father give him?**

   Number sentence: _____

   Model:

   Solution: _____

STOP

Mathematics

| M5A1 |

Algebra

Investigating
Algebraic Expressions

Example:

Let $w = -2$, $y = 3$, and $z = \dfrac{1}{2}$

Then $w(2z - 4y) = -2(2 \times \dfrac{1}{2} - 4 \times 3)$

$$= -2(1 - 12)$$
$$= -2 \times -11$$
$$= 22$$

DIRECTIONS: Draw conclusions about the following expressions, if $w = \dfrac{1}{3}$, $y = 4$, and $z = -2$.

1. $3w =$

2. $y + z =$

3. $y - z =$

4. $w(8 + y) =$

5. $6zw =$

6. $3(y + z) - 6w =$

DIRECTIONS: Draw conclusions about the same expressions, if $w = \dfrac{1}{2}$, $y = 8$, and $z = -3$.

7. $3w =$

8. $y + z =$

9. $y - z =$

10. $w(8 + y) =$

11. $6zw =$

12. $3(y + z) - 6w =$

STOP

Georgia Test Practice

Mathematics

M5D1

Analyzing Data in Graphs

DIRECTIONS: The tally chart shows the hair color of some fifth-grade students. Choose the best answer.

Brown	Black	Blond	Red

1. **Which of these questions could you answer using the information on the tally chart?**

   Ⓐ How often do the students get their hair cut?

   Ⓑ How many students dye their hair?

   Ⓒ Which students have long hair?

   Ⓓ How many more brown-haired students are there than blond-haired students?

2. **Which graph below shows the data on the tally chart?**

   Ⓕ
   Brown Black Blond Red

   Ⓖ
   Brown Black Blond Red

   Ⓗ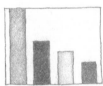
   Brown Black Blond Red

   Ⓙ
   Brown Black Blond Red

3. **Which circle shows the shaded fraction of the students on the tally chart that have black hair?**

   Ⓐ

   Ⓑ

   Ⓒ

   Ⓓ

4. **Which type of chart or graph best illustrates percentages?**

   Ⓕ tally charts

   Ⓖ bar graphs

   Ⓗ circle graphs

   Ⓙ line graphs

STOP

Mathematics
| M5D2 |

Using Appropriate Graphs

DIRECTIONS: The same data can be represented in different ways depending on which style of chart is used. Use the information in the following table to fill in the bar graph and circle chart below.

School Election Results				
Grade	Votes for Blue Party	Votes for Red Party	Total Votes by Grade	Percentage of Total Votes
Third	25	5	30	33%
Fourth	10	16	26	28%
Fifth	15	21	36	39%
Total Votes by Party	50	42		

1. **School Election Results**

2. **Voters in Each Grade**

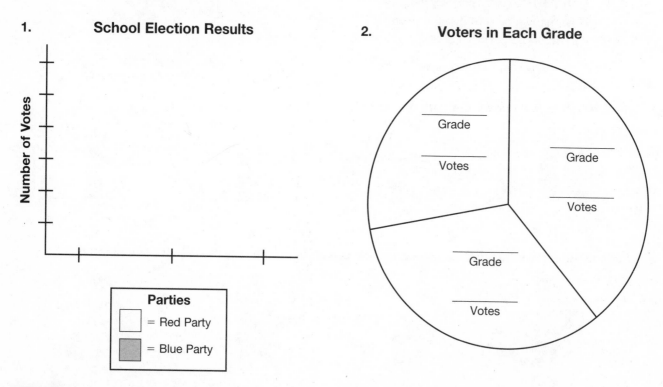

DIRECTIONS: Use the data below to construct a graph of your choice. Then briefly explain why this is an appropriate graph to use for this data.

3.

Favorite Musical Styles Among Fifth Graders	
Pop	25%
Rock	10%
Rap	30%
Country	20%
Other	15%

Mathematics

M5G/M5A/M5D

For pages 103–108

Geometry, Algebra, and Data Analysis

Mini-Test 3

DIRECTIONS: Choose the best answer.

1. **Look at the circle. What does the line segment AB represent?**

   Ⓐ radius
   Ⓑ diameter
   Ⓒ area
   Ⓓ circumference

   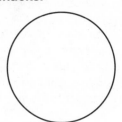

2. **A survey was done of fans at a baseball game. The fans voted on their favorite ballgame snack. The results of the survey are below. Make a circle graph to represent their favorite types of snacks.**

   peanuts 15%

   ice cream 20%

   popcorn 25%

   nachos 10%

   hot dogs 30%

3. **Which snack in question 2 was the most popular?**

   Ⓕ hot dogs
   Ⓖ popcorn
   Ⓗ ice cream
   Ⓙ peanuts

4. **Which snack in question 2 was the least popular?**

   Ⓐ hot dogs
   Ⓑ popcorn
   Ⓒ nachos
   Ⓓ peanuts

5. **What value does *b* have to be to make both equations true?**

   $$b - 7 = 15; 2 \times 11 = b$$

   Ⓕ 85
   Ⓖ 12
   Ⓗ 21
   Ⓙ 22

6. **In which of these equations is *y* equal to 7?**

   Ⓐ $15 \div 8 = y$
   Ⓑ $y + 15 = 8$
   Ⓒ $y + 8 = 15$
   Ⓓ $8 \times y = 15$

7. **Which pair of shapes is congruent?**

   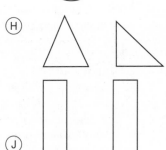

   Ⓕ

   Ⓖ

   Ⓗ

   Ⓙ

STOP

Process Skills Standards

M5P. Process Skills

Students will apply mathematical concepts and skills in the context of authentic problems and will understand concepts rather than merely following a sequence of procedures. Students will use the process standards as a way of acquiring and using content knowledge.

M5P1. Using the appropriate technology, students will solve problems that arise in mathematics and in other contexts. *(See pages 111–112.)*
a. Solve nonroutine word problems using the strategy of make it simpler as well as all strategies learned in previous grades.
b. Solve single- and multi-step routine word problems related to all appropriate fifth-grade math standards.
c. Determine the operation(s) needed to solve a problem.
d. Determine the most efficient way to solve a problem (mental math, paper/pencil, or calculator).

What it means:

- When presented with a math problem, students should be able to gather the correct information, in the correct order, and apply relevant mathematical concepts. For example, given the problem: *Six cases of pears and five cases of peaches are delivered to the school cafeteria. Each case contains 12 cans. The peaches are in 32-ounce cans, and the pears are in 64-ounce cans. How many cans of pears are there?* Students should determine that they will need to use multiplication to determine the answer. Irrelevant information includes the number of cases of peaches and the size of the cans.

M5P2. Students will investigate, develop, and evaluate mathematical arguments. *(See page 113.)*

M5P3. Students will use the language of mathematics to express ideas precisely. *(See page 114.)*

What it means:

- Relating informal language to mathematical language and symbols means that students will be able to turn a word problem into a mathematical situation. For example, students should understand that the words "less than" indicate that they will need to subtract.

M5P4. Students will understand how mathematical ideas interconnect and build on one another and apply mathematics in other content areas. *(See page 115.)*

M5P5. Students will create and use pictures, manipulatives, models, and symbols to organize, record, and communicate mathematical ideas. *(See page 116.)*

Mathematics

M5P1

Solving Problems

DIRECTIONS: Choose the best answer.

 Clue You might find it helpful to use scratch paper to draw pictures or record information to solve many of these problems.

1. Two numbers have a product of 108 and a quotient of 12. What are the two numbers?

   (A) 9, 12

   (B) 7, 16

   (C) 36, 3

   (D) 54, 6

2. There are several uninvited ants at a picnic in the park. Among the 9 guests that are ants or people, there are 30 legs altogether. How many ants are at the picnic?

   (F) 9 ants

   (G) 6 ants

   (H) 4 ants

   (J) 3 ants

3. Mr. Grace found three programs that he wanted to buy for the classroom. *Math Busters* was $21.80. *Spelling Practice* was $16.85. *Reading Classics* was $13.65. He spent a total of $35.45. What programs did he buy?

   (A) *Math Busters* and *Spelling Practice*

   (B) *Math Busters* and *Reading Classics*

   (C) *Spelling Practice* and *Reading Classics*

   (D) none of these

4. Carla has 6 hockey cards. Ed and Carla together have 16 hockey cards. Judith and Ed together have 25 hockey cards. How many hockey cards does Judith have?

   (F) 6 hockey cards

   (G) 9 hockey cards

   (H) 15 hockey cards

   (J) 20 hockey cards

5. The number of people watching a hockey game is 900 when rounded to the nearest hundred and 850 when rounded to the nearest ten. Which of these could be the number of people watching the game?

   (A) 847 people

   (B) 849 people

   (C) 856 people

   (D) 852 people

6. The Card Shop receives a shipment of trading cards each month. There are 8 hockey cards in a pack, 12 packs in a box, and 16 boxes in a shipping crate. Which is the total number of hockey cards in the shipping crate?

   (F) 1,536 hockey cards

   (G) 672 hockey cards

   (H) 1,436 hockey cards

   (J) 662 hockey cards

7. After the hockey game, each of these players bought a can of soda from a machine that takes both coins and bills. The soda costs 70¢ per can.

   Luke used only dimes.

   Jacques used only quarters.

   Pierre used only half-dollars.

   Roland used a dollar bill.

   Which two players got the same amount of change?

   (A) Luke and Jacques

   (B) Jacques and Pierre

   (C) Pierre and Roland

   (D) Roland and Luke

Mathematics

M5P1

Determining Operations Needed to Solve Problems

DIRECTIONS: Choose the best answer.

1. There are 324 students in the fifth grade. Each student pledged to read 50 books during the year. Which number sentence shows how to find the number of books the fifth graders pledged to read?

   (A) $324 \div 50 = \blacksquare$

   (B) $324 \times 50 = \blacksquare$

   (C) $324 + 50 = \blacksquare$

   (D) $324 - 50 = \blacksquare$

2. The amounts below show how much a student earned during a six-week time period. What operations are necessary to find out the student's average weekly earnings?

$41.87	$36.23	$25.90
$42.36	$34.21	$27.83

   (F) subtraction and addition

   (G) addition and multiplication

   (H) addition and division

   (J) multiplication and division

3. What is the number sentence for determining the volume of a rectangular prism that measures 3 units long, 5 units wide, and 8 units high?

   (A) $3 \times 5 \times 8 = \blacksquare$

   (B) $3 + 5 + 8 = \blacksquare$

   (C) $(3 \times 5) + 8 = \blacksquare$

   (D) $(3 + 5) \times 8 = \blacksquare$

4. The art instructor is paid $15 per hour. She works for 6 hours a day. Which number sentence shows how to find the amount she earns in one day?

   (F) $15 + 6 = \blacksquare$

   (G) $15 - 6 = \blacksquare$

   (H) $15 \times 6 = \blacksquare$

   (J) $15 \div 6 = \blacksquare$

5. Suppose you wanted to double the number 8 and then add 10 to it. Which number sentence would you use?

   (A) $(8 \times 2) + 10 = \blacksquare$

   (B) $8 + 2 + 10 = \blacksquare$

   (C) $8 \times 2 \times 10 = \blacksquare$

   (D) $(2 \times 10) + 8 = \blacksquare$

6. How do you find the perimeter of a rectangle?

   (F) Square the length of one side.

   (G) Subtract the length of the shortest side from the length of the longest side.

   (H) Multiply the base times the height.

   (J) Add the lengths of all sides.

STOP

Mathematics

M5P2

Developing Mathematical Arguments

DIRECTIONS: Choose the best answer.

1. Monica ate $\frac{1}{8}$ of her sandwich for lunch, Sam ate $\frac{2}{3}$ of his apple, and Rick drank all of his milk. How much of her milk did Monica drink?

  (A) $\frac{1}{8}$ of the milk

  (B) $\frac{2}{3}$ of the milk

  (C) all of the milk

  (D) not enough information

2. There were 258 cans of soup on the grocery store shelf in the morning. At 1:00 P.M., there were 156 cans of soup on the shelf. By the time the store closed at 7:00 P.M., several more cans of soup had been sold. How many cans of soup did the store sell in the entire day?

  (F) 102 cans

  (G) 288 cans

  (H) 414 cans

  (J) not enough information

3. Sasha went to the park at 9:30 A.M. She played for 45 minutes and then started soccer practice. She had soccer practice for 90 minutes. At what time did soccer practice end?

  (A) 10:45 A.M.

  (B) 11:15 A.M.

  (C) 11:45 A.M.

  (D) not enough information

4. Jessica must find the area of a square with one side that is 12 inches long. How can Jessica figure it out?

  (F) She can add all the sides together.

  (G) She can multiply 2 sides together.

  (H) She can divide 2 sides by each other.

  (J) She cannot figure out the area with the information she has.

5. Mavis works at the hardware store. Her hourly wage is $4.50. How much money is Mavis paid for one week's work? Which piece of information will help you solve this problem?

  (A) the number of hours she works each day

  (B) the number of days she works each week

  (C) the number of hours she works each week

  (D) the address of the hardware store

6. At the school store, José bought 2 pencils for $0.10 each, a notebook for $0.65, and a candy bar for $0.40. To find out how much change he will get, you need to know _____ .

  (F) how much 2 notebooks cost

  (G) how much money he gave the salesperson

  (H) how much he saved by buying one notebook

  (J) how much money he has

STOP

Mathematics

M5P3 **Using Mathematical Language**

DIRECTIONS: Choose the best answer.

Example:

The Florida State Fair is held every year in Tampa. At one of the state fairs, there were 48 Girl Scouts marching in the parade. There were 6 girls in each row. Which equation would you use to find how many rows of Girl Scouts were marching in the parade?

- (A) $48 + 6 = n$
- (B) $n \times 6 = 48$
- (C) $48 - n = 6$
- (D) $48 \times 6 = n$

Answer: (B)

1. A factory has 314 workers. The owner gave a total bonus of $612,300. Which number sentence shows how to find the amount of bonus money each worker received? Let b = amount of bonus money.

- (A) $b + 314 = \$612{,}300$
- (B) $b \times 314 = \$612{,}300$
- (C) $b - 314 = \$612{,}300$
- (D) $b \div 314 = \$612{,}300$

2. The human heart pumps about 24 liters of blood in 5 minutes. You want to know about how many liters of blood are pumped in 1 minute. Which math problem will help you find the answer?

- (F) $24 \div 5 = \blacksquare$
- (G) $24 \times 5 = \blacksquare$
- (H) $24 + 5 = \blacksquare$
- (J) $24 - 5 = \blacksquare$

3. A flea can jump 130 times its own height. If you could do the same thing, and your height is 54 inches, how high could you jump? Which math problem could help you find the answer?

- (A) $130 + 54 = \blacksquare$
- (B) $130 - 54 = \blacksquare$
- (C) $130 \div 54 = \blacksquare$
- (D) $130 \times 54 = \blacksquare$

4. Joyce collects football cards. She puts them into stacks of 9 cards each. She has 36 stacks of cards. She wants to know how many cards she has in all. Which computation shows how to find the correct answer?

- (F) $36 + 9 = 45$
- (G) $36 \times 9 = 324$
- (H) $36 \div 9 = 4$
- (J) $36 - 9 = 27$

5. LaToya has 72 books in her collection. She wants to put only 8 books on each of her shelves. Which expression could she use to figure out how many shelves she will need for her books?

- (A) $72 + 8 = s$
- (B) $72 - 8 = s$
- (C) $72 \div 8 = s$
- (D) $s \div 8 = 72$

6. Marlo drove 350 miles in 7 hours and used 17.5 gallons of gas. How do you determine her speed?

- (F) $350 \times 7 \div 17.5$
- (G) $350 \div 17.5$
- (H) 17.5×7
- (J) $350 \div 7$

STOP

M5P4

Applying Math in Other Areas

Clue Math is often used in other subject areas, such as science, history, and geography.

DIRECTIONS: Read the graph showing the number of herons on Ash Pond. Then answer questions 1–2.

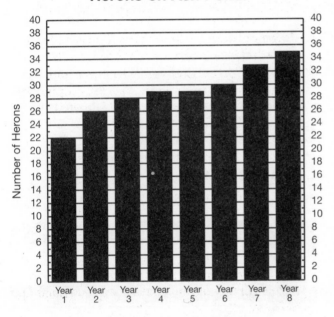

Herons on Ash Pond

1. **Based on the data, how much did the heron population increase between year 1 and year 8?**

   Ⓐ by 22
   Ⓑ by 13
   Ⓒ by 12
   Ⓓ by 57

2. **Based on the data, what could you predict for year 11?**

   Ⓕ The number of herons will increase.
   Ⓖ The number of herons will decrease.
   Ⓗ The number of herons will stay the same.
   Ⓙ Herons will become endangered.

DIRECTIONS: This pictograph shows how many people immigrated to the United States from 1820 to 1920. Each 🚶 stands for 1,000,000 immigrants. Use the pictograph to answer question 3.

Number of People Who Immigrated to the U.S.	
1820–1840	🚶
1841–1860	🚶🚶🚶🚶
1861–1880	🚶🚶🚶🚶🚶
1881–1900	🚶🚶🚶🚶🚶🚶🚶🚶
1901–1920	🚶🚶🚶🚶🚶🚶🚶🚶🚶🚶🚶

3. **During which years did the greatest number of people immigrate?**

_____

DIRECTIONS: About 16 million people live in Florida. About how many of them live in cities?

4. **Use the graph below to answer question 4.**

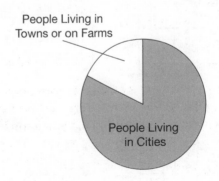

People Living in Towns or on Farms

People Living in Cities

   Ⓐ 14 million
   Ⓑ 8 million
   Ⓒ 5 million
   Ⓓ 3 million

Mathematics
M5P5   **Using Pictures and Models**

DIRECTIONS: Choose the best answer.

1. Which figure below is $\frac{4}{9}$ shaded?

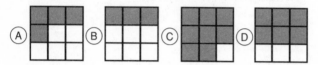

2. The length of YZ is what fraction of the length of VX?

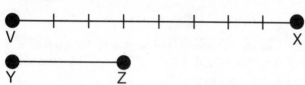

Ⓕ $\frac{7}{12}$

Ⓖ $\frac{5}{10}$

Ⓗ $\frac{4}{8}$

Ⓙ $\frac{3}{8}$

3. Tenisha just made a number chart on which she shaded all the multiples of 5. Which pattern shows the shading on her number chart?

Ⓐ 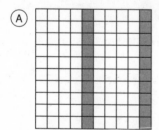   Ⓑ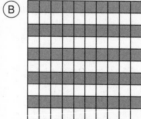

Ⓒ 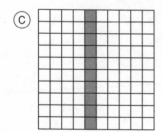   Ⓓ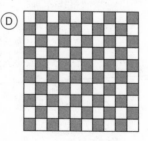

4. Which number tells how much of this group of shapes is shaded?

Ⓕ $\frac{3}{4}$

Ⓖ $3\frac{1}{2}$

Ⓗ $3\frac{1}{4}$

Ⓙ $3\frac{3}{4}$

DIRECTIONS: There are five classes of fifth graders at the Tropicana School: Classes 5-1, 5-2, 5-3, 5-4, and 5-5. A different teacher teaches each class. The number of students in each class is represented by the pictograph below. Each ☺ means 8 students. Use the pictograph to answer question 5.

Class	Teacher	Number of Students
5-1	Miss Apple	☺ ☺ ☺ ◖
5-2	Mr. Kiwi	☺ ☺ ☺ ◗
5-3	Ms. Melon	☺ ☺ ☺ ◹
5-4	Mr. Cranberry	☺ ☺ ◖
5-5	Miss Mango	☺ ☺ ☺ ☺

5. Which teacher has 30 students?

Ⓐ Miss Apple

Ⓑ Mr. Kiwi

Ⓒ Ms. Melon

Ⓓ Mr. Cranberry

STOP

Mathematics   Process Skills

| M5P1–M5P5 |

Mini-Test 4

For pages 111–116

DIRECTIONS: Choose the best answer.

1. A librarian was putting books on shelves. There were 58 books and 6 shelves. The librarian wanted to put the same number of books on each shelf, but she had some extras. How many books did not fit on the 6 shelves?

- Ⓐ 4 books
- Ⓑ 6 books
- Ⓒ 8 books
- Ⓓ 9 books

2. Regina has $2.33 in coins. She has 6 quarters, 5 dimes, 2 nickels, and the rest in pennies. How many pennies does Regina have?

- Ⓕ 12 pennies
- Ⓖ 33 pennies
- Ⓗ 17 pennies
- Ⓙ 23 pennies

3. Clarissa was paid $204 for 3 days of work. She worked 8 hours each day. What was her rate?

- Ⓐ $8.50 per hour
- Ⓑ $8.50 per day
- Ⓒ $25.50 per day
- Ⓓ $68 per hour

4. Bicycle speedometers are programmed based on the number of revolutions the wheel turns per second. A bike wheel spins 480 times in 1 minute. What is the rate per second?

- Ⓕ 1 revolution per second
- Ⓖ 8 revolutions per second
- Ⓗ 60 revolutions per second
- Ⓙ 480 revolutions per second

5. If each 😊 stands for 3 people, how would you show 12 people?

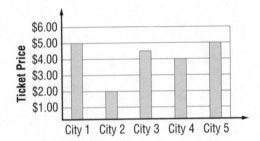

- Ⓓ none of these

DIRECTIONS: The graph below shows the cost of a ticket to the movies in five different cities. Use the graph for questions 6–8.

6. In what city is the ticket price lowest?

- Ⓕ City 1
- Ⓖ City 2
- Ⓗ City 3
- Ⓙ City 4

7. Which cities have the same ticket price?

- Ⓐ Cities 1 and 3
- Ⓑ Cities 3 and 5
- Ⓒ Cities 1 and 5
- Ⓓ Cities 4 and 5

8. What is the ticket price in City 3?

- Ⓕ $5.00
- Ⓖ $3.50
- Ⓗ $4.00
- Ⓙ $4.50

STOP

How Am I Doing?

Mini-Test 1 Page 92 **Number Correct**	**8–9** answers correct	**Great Job!** Move on to the section test on page 120.
	5–7 answers correct	**You're almost there!** But you still need a little practice. Review practice pages 82–91 before moving on to the section test on page 120.
	0–4 answers correct	**Oops!** Time to review what you have learned and try again. Review the practice section on pages 82–91. Then retake the test on page 92. Now move on to the section test on page 120.
Mini-Test 2 Page 101 **Number Correct**	**8** answers correct	**Awesome!** Move on to the section test on page 120.
	5–7 answers correct	**You're almost there!** But you still need a little practice. Review practice pages 94–100 before moving on to the section test on page 120.
	0–4 answers correct	**Oops!** Time to review what you have learned and try again. Review the practice section on pages 94–100. Then retake the test on page 101. Now move on to the section test on page 120.
Mini-Test 3 Page 109 **Number Correct**	**7** answers correct	**Great Job!** Move on to the section test on page 120.
	5–6 answers correct	**You're almost there!** But you still need a little practice. Review practice pages 103–108 before moving on to the section test on page 120.
	0–4 answers correct	**Oops!** Time to review what you have learned and try again. Review the practice section on pages 103–108. Then retake the test on page 109. Now move on to the section test on page 120.

How Am I Doing?

Mini-Test 4	8 answers correct	**Awesome!** Move on to the section test on page 120.
Page 117 **Number Correct**	5–7 answers correct	**You're almost there!** But you still need a little practice. Review practice pages 111–116 before moving on to the section test on page 120.
	0–4 answers correct	**Oops!** Time to review what you have learned and try again. Review the practice section on pages 111–116. Then retake the test on page 117. Now move on to the section test on page 120.

Name _____ Date _____

Final Mathematics Test
for pages 82–116

DIRECTIONS: Choose the best answer.

1. **Which group of decimals is ordered from least to greatest?**

   Ⓐ 3.332, 3.321, 3.295, 3.287, 3.111

   Ⓑ 3.424, 3.425, 3.339, 3.383, 3.214

   Ⓒ 3.109, 3.107, 3.278, 3.229, 3.344

   Ⓓ 3.132, 3.234, 3.262, 3.391, 3.406

2. **Which of the following is not equivalent to the shaded portion of the figure?**

   Ⓕ $\dfrac{1}{3}$

   Ⓖ $\dfrac{2}{6}$

   Ⓗ $\dfrac{12}{36}$

   Ⓙ 30%

   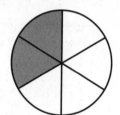

3. **Cole and Jenny split a candy bar. Cole ate $\dfrac{3}{16}$ and Jenny ate $\dfrac{11}{16}$. Who ate more? Did they eat the whole candy bar?**

   Ⓐ Cole, yes

   Ⓑ Jenny, yes

   Ⓒ Cole, no

   Ⓓ Jenny, no

4. **It took Scott $\dfrac{3}{6}$ of an hour to get home. What is the decimal equivalent of $\dfrac{3}{6}$?**

   Ⓕ 0.5

   Ⓖ 0.36

   Ⓗ 2.0

   Ⓙ none of these

5. **Lucinda has $1.00 to buy pencils that cost 14 cents each. How many pencils can she buy?**

   Ⓐ 14 pencils

   Ⓑ 86 pencils

   Ⓒ 7 pencils

   Ⓓ 114 pencils

6. **The stakes in Jack's croquet set are 2 feet long. He drove one stake $\dfrac{3}{4}$ foot into the ground. How much of the stake is above ground?**

   Ⓕ $1\dfrac{1}{4}$ feet

   Ⓖ 2 feet

   Ⓗ $\dfrac{3}{4}$ foot

   Ⓙ 1 foot

7. **Which of the following figures represents a prime number?**

   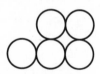

   Figure A   **Figure B**

   Ⓐ They are both prime.

   Ⓑ Figure A

   Ⓒ Figure B

   Ⓓ Neither is prime.

8. **Write 26 as the product of its prime factors.**

   Ⓕ 2 × 6

   Ⓖ 2 × 13

   Ⓗ 2 × 2 × 3 × 3

   Ⓙ 4 × 9

GO

Georgia Test Practice

9. What is the approximate area of this shape?

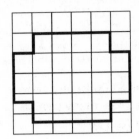

- (A) 16 square units
- (B) 18 square units
- (C) 20 square units
- (D) 23 square units

10. What is the area of this circle?

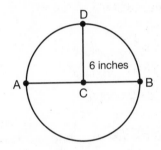

6 inches

- (F) 18.84 in.²
- (G) 36 in.²
- (H) 37.68 in.²
- (J) 113.04 in.²

11. What is the area of this parallelogram?

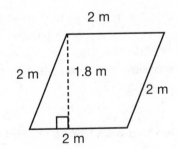

2 m
2 m
1.8 m
2 m
2 m

- (A) 1.8 m²
- (B) 3.6 m²
- (C) 4 m²
- (D) 8 m²

12. Which of the following amounts is the largest?

- (F) 16 fluid ounces
- (G) 1 pint
- (H) 3 cups
- (J) $\frac{1}{2}$ quart

13. $4 \frac{1}{2}$ gallons = _____

- (A) 18 quarts
- (B) 20 quarts
- (C) 40 quarts
- (D) 80 cups

14. What is the volume of this figure?

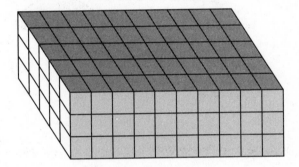

- (F) 150 cubic units
- (G) 100 cubic units
- (H) 53 cubic units
- (J) 50 cubic units

15. What is the volume of this figure?

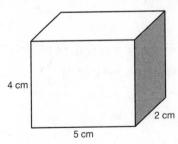

4 cm
2 cm
5 cm

- (A) 10 cm³
- (B) 20 cm³
- (C) 40 cm³
- (D) 80 cm³

GO

16. Which of the figures below are congruent?

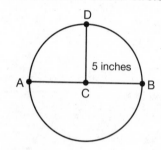

A   B   C   D

- (F) B and C
- (G) A and C
- (H) B and D
- (J) A and D

17. What is the diameter of the circle?

5 inches

- (A) 5 inches
- (B) 10 inches
- (C) 31.4 inches
- (D) none of these

18. What value does *b* have to make both equations true?

$$b - 9 = 15; 2 \times 12 = b$$

- (F) 22
- (G) 23
- (H) 24
- (J) 30

19. In which of these is *y* equal to 9?

- (A) $17 \div 8 = y$
- (B) $y + 17 = 8$
- (C) $y + 8 = 17$
- (D) $8 \times y = 17$

DIRECTIONS: Choose the best answer. Use the bar graph for questions 20–21.

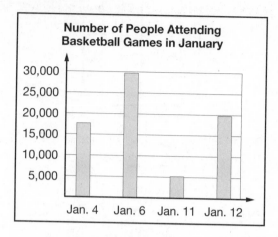

Number of People Attending Basketball Games in January

30,000
25,000
20,000
15,000
10,000
5,000

Jan. 4   Jan. 6   Jan. 11   Jan. 12

20. How many more people attended the Jan. 6 game than the Jan. 12 game?

- (F) 10,000 people
- (G) 8,000 people
- (H) 5,000 people
- (J) 2,000 people

21. On one of the dates, a snowstorm prevented many people from going to the game. On which date did the storm occur?

- (A) Jan. 12
- (B) Jan. 4
- (C) Jan. 11
- (D) Jan. 6

22. The Spanish Club wants to buy a set of instructional videos. Each video costs $12.50. What information will they need to determine how much money they must raise to buy the entire set of videos?

- (F) the number of students in the school
- (G) how long each video is
- (H) the number of videos in the set
- (J) how many students there are in the Spanish Club

GO

23. An auto mechanic earns $19 an hour. She works
8 hours a day. Which number sentence shows
how to find how much she earns in a day?

Ⓐ 19 + 8 = ■

Ⓑ 19 − 8 = ■

Ⓒ 19 × 8 = ■

Ⓓ 19 ÷ 8 = ■

24. Which of these number sentences would help
you find the total number of flags?

Ⓕ 5 + 3 = ■

Ⓖ 5 − 3 = ■

Ⓖ 5 × 3 = ■

Ⓗ 5 ÷ 3 = ■

25. A waterproof jacket costs $49.95. The cold-
weather lining for the jacket is $22.50 and
a matching hat is $12.75. How much would
it cost to buy the jacket and liner, but not
the hat?

Ⓐ $85.20

Ⓑ $72.45

Ⓒ $61.45

Ⓓ $62.70

DIRECTIONS: A survey on favorite colors was taken at
Rosa's school. The graph below shows the results
of the survey. Study the graph, and then answer
questions 26–27.

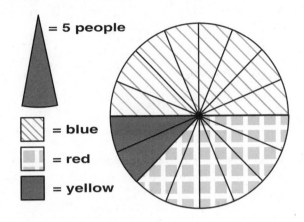

= 5 people

= blue

= red

= yellow

26. How many more students prefer the color red
over yellow?

Ⓕ 4 students

Ⓖ 12 students

Ⓗ 20 students

Ⓙ 35 students

27. How many students chose blue as their
favorite color?

Ⓐ 8 students

Ⓑ 50 students

Ⓒ 24 students

Ⓓ 40 students

STOP

Name _____ Date _____

Final Mathematics Test
Answer Sheet

1 Ⓐ Ⓑ Ⓒ Ⓓ
2 Ⓕ Ⓖ Ⓗ Ⓙ
3 Ⓐ Ⓑ Ⓒ Ⓓ
4 Ⓕ Ⓖ Ⓗ Ⓙ
5 Ⓐ Ⓑ Ⓒ Ⓓ
6 Ⓕ Ⓖ Ⓗ Ⓙ
7 Ⓐ Ⓑ Ⓒ Ⓓ
8 Ⓕ Ⓖ Ⓗ Ⓙ
9 Ⓐ Ⓑ Ⓒ Ⓓ
10 Ⓕ Ⓖ Ⓗ Ⓙ

11 Ⓐ Ⓑ Ⓒ Ⓓ
12 Ⓕ Ⓖ Ⓗ Ⓙ
13 Ⓐ Ⓑ Ⓒ Ⓓ
14 Ⓕ Ⓖ Ⓗ Ⓙ
15 Ⓐ Ⓑ Ⓒ Ⓓ
16 Ⓕ Ⓖ Ⓗ Ⓙ
17 Ⓐ Ⓑ Ⓒ Ⓓ
18 Ⓕ Ⓖ Ⓗ Ⓙ
19 Ⓐ Ⓑ Ⓒ Ⓓ
20 Ⓕ Ⓖ Ⓗ Ⓙ

21 Ⓐ Ⓑ Ⓒ Ⓓ
22 Ⓕ Ⓖ Ⓗ Ⓙ
23 Ⓐ Ⓑ Ⓒ Ⓓ
24 Ⓕ Ⓖ Ⓗ Ⓙ
25 Ⓐ Ⓑ Ⓒ Ⓓ
26 Ⓕ Ⓖ Ⓗ Ⓙ
27 Ⓐ Ⓑ Ⓒ Ⓓ

Georgia Social Studies
Content Standards

The social studies section measures knowledge in four different areas:

1) History

2) Geography

3) Government/Civics

4) Economics

Georgia Social Studies
Table of Contents

History Standards

SS5H1. The student will explain the causes, major events, and consequences of the Civil War. *(See pages 128–129.)*

a. Identify *Uncle Tom's Cabin* and John Brown's raid on Harpers Ferry, and explain how each of these events was related to the Civil War.

b. Discuss how the issues of states' rights and slavery increased tensions between the North and South.

c. Identify major battles and campaigns: Fort Sumter, Gettysburg, the Atlanta Campaign, Sherman's March to the Sea, Appomattox Court House.

d. Describe the roles of Abraham Lincoln, Robert E. Lee, Ulysses S. Grant, Jefferson Davis, and Thomas "Stonewall" Jackson.

e. Describe the effects of war on the North and South.

SS5H2. The student will analyze the effects of Reconstruction on American life. *(See page 130.)*

a. Describe the purpose of the Thirteenth, Fourteenth, and Fifteenth Amendments.

b. Explain the work of the Freedmen's Bureau.

c. Explain how slavery was replaced by sharecropping and how African Americans were prevented from exercising their newly-won rights, including Jim Crow laws and customs.

SS5H3. The student will describe how life changed in America at the turn of the Century. *(See pages 131–132.)*

a. Describe the role of the cattle trails in the late nineteenth century, including the Black Cowboys of Texas, the Great Western Cattle Trail, and the Chisholm Trail.

b. Describe the impact on American life of the Wright brothers (flight), George Washington Carver (science), Alexander Graham Bell (communication), and Thomas Edison (electricity).

c. Explain how William McKinley and Theodore Roosevelt expanded America's role in the world, including the Spanish-American War and the building of the Panama Canal.

d. Describe the reasons people emigrated to the United States, from where they emigrated, and where they settled.

SS5H4. The student will describe the U.S. involvement in World War I and post–World War I America. *(See pages 133–134.)*

a. Explain how German attacks on U.S. shipping during the war in Europe (1914–1917) ultimately led the United States to join the fight against Germany, including the sinking of the *Lusitania* and concerns over safety of U.S. ships.

b. Describe the cultural developments and individual contributions in the 1920s of the Jazz Age (Louis Armstrong), the Harlem Renaissance (Langston Hughes), baseball (Babe Ruth), the automobile (Henry Ford), and the airplane (Charles Lindbergh).

SS5H5. The student will explain how the Great Depression and New Deal affected the lives of millions of Americans. *(See pages 135–136.)*

a. Discuss the Stock Market Crash of 1929, Herbert Hoover, Franklin Roosevelt, the Dust Bowl, and soup kitchens.

b. Analyze the main features of the New Deal including the significance of the Civilian Conservation Corps, Works Progress Administration, and the Tennessee Valley Authority.

c. Discuss important cultural elements of the 1930s, including Duke Ellington, Margaret Mitchell, and Jesse Owens.

History Standards

SS5H6. The student will explain the reasons for America's involvement in World War II. *(See pages 137–138.)*
a. Describe Germany's aggression in Europe and Japan's aggression in Asia.
b. Describe major events in the war in both Europe and the Pacific, including Pearl Harbor, Iwo Jima, D-Day, V-E and V-J Days, and the Holocaust.
c. Discuss President Truman's decision to drop the atomic bomb on Hiroshima and Nagasaki.
d. Identify Roosevelt, Stalin, Churchill, Hirohito, Truman, Mussolini, and Hitler.
e. Describe the effects of rationing and the changing role of women and African Americans, including "Rosie the Riveter" and the Tuskegee Airmen.
f. Explain the U.S. role in the formation of the United Nations.

SS5H7. The student will discuss the origins and consequences of the Cold War. *(See page 139.)*
a. Explain the origin and meaning of the term "Iron Curtain."
b. Explain how the United States sought to stop the spread of communism through the Berlin airlift, the Korean War, and the North Atlantic Treaty Organization.
c. Identify Joseph McCarthy and Nikita Khrushchev.

SS5H8. The student will describe the importance of key people, events, and developments between 1950–1975. *(See pages 140–141.)*
a. Discuss the importance of the Cuban Missile Crisis and the Vietnam War.
b. Explain the key events and people of the Civil Rights movement, including *Brown v. Board of Education* 1954, Montgomery Bus Boycott, the March on Washington, Civil Rights Act and Voting Rights Act, and civil rights activities of Thurgood Marshall, Rosa Parks, and Martin Luther King, Jr.
c. Describe the impact on American society of the assassinations of President John F. Kennedy, Robert F. Kennedy, and Martin Luther King, Jr.
d. Discuss the significance of the new technologies of television and space exploration.

SS5H9. The student will trace important developments in America since 1975. *(See page 142.)*
a. Describe U.S. involvement in world events, including efforts to bring peace to the Middle East, the collapse of the Soviet Union, the Persian Gulf War, and the War on Terrorism in response to September 11, 2001.
b. Explain the impact the development of the personal computer and Internet have had on American life.

Name _____   Date _____

SS5H1

The Causes, Events, and Effects of the Civil War

DIRECTIONS: Match each of the people below to the correct description.

1. _____ **Jefferson Davis**

2. _____ **Ulysses S. Grant**

3. _____ **Thomas "Stonewall" Jackson**

4. _____ **Robert E. Lee**

5. _____ **Abraham Lincoln**

6. _____ **Harriet Beecher Stowe**

a. U.S. president during the Civil War

b. author of *Uncle Tom's Cabin*

c. commander of the Confederate army

d. commander of the Union army

e. president of the Confederacy

f. Confederate general famous for his victories in the Shenandoah Valley

DIRECTIONS: Choose the best answer.

7. **Where did the Civil War begin?**
   - (A) Harpers Ferry
   - (B) Bull Run
   - (C) Fort Sumter
   - (D) Gettysburg

8. **What Civil War battle was fought in Pennsylvania?**
   - (F) Fredericksburg
   - (G) Vicksburg
   - (H) Antietam
   - (J) Gettysburg

9. **Which Union general captured Atlanta?**
   - (A) Grant
   - (B) Sherman
   - (C) Sheridan
   - (D) Meade

10. **Where did General Lee surrender to General Grant?**
    - (F) Gettysburg
    - (G) Appomattox Court House
    - (H) Antietam
    - (J) Chancellorsville

11. **Sherman's destructive advance from Atlanta to Savannah is referred to as the _____ .**
    - (A) March to the Sea
    - (B) Anaconda Plan
    - (C) Bloody Lane
    - (D) Final Siege

12. **The publication of *Uncle Tom's Cabin* contributed to the start of the Civil War by _____ .**
    - (F) showing the evils of slavery
    - (G) condemning abolitionists
    - (H) supporting states' rights
    - (J) supporting the rights of slaveholders

GO

13. The raid on Harpers Ferry convinced many Southerners that _____ .

- (A) slavery should be abolished
- (B) John Brown was a hero
- (C) abolitionists were not a serious threat
- (D) they needed to secede, or withdraw, from the Union

14. Southerners justified secession with the theory of _____ .

- (F) constitutional rights
- (G) federal rights
- (H) states' rights
- (J) the Union's errors

15. The Civil War was more devastating in the South than in the North because _____ .

- (A) most of the fighting took place in the South
- (B) the blockade of Southern ports caused severe shortages
- (C) the South lacked the industry to produce what it needed
- (D) all of the above

DIRECTIONS: Read the passage below and then choose the best answer.

For a long time in this country, slavery was accepted. George Washington, this nation's first president, had over 200 slaves. In fact, eight of the first 12 presidents were slaveholders.

From the beginning, some Americans thought slavery was wrong. Most of the people who opposed slavery lived in the northern half of the nation. Many people in the South supported slavery. In the South, a plantation's success or failure might depend on the slaves who worked there.

The rocky soil of New England did not encourage great big farms. So, New England farmers could, with the help of their families, farm their own fields. They had little use for slaves. In addition, many mills and factories were being built in the North. That meant fewer Northerners were making their living by farming.

In the South, giant plantations grew up. Some of the crops grown on a plantation needed a great deal

of care. Tobacco especially took a lot of work. The southern farmer needed help farming his many acres of crops. The least expensive year-round help he could get was a slave.

16. Based on the passage, which of the following statements is *not* true?

- (F) Slavery was accepted in this country for many years.
- ✓ (G) Several presidents were slaveholders.
- (H) There were a lot of plantations in the North that required the use of slaves to care for the crops.
- (J) Most people who opposed slavery lived in the northern half of the nation.

17. From this passage you can predict that slavery became most important to the _____ economy in the United States.

- (A) Western
- ✓ (B) Southern
- (C) Northern
- (D) Midwestern

DIRECTIONS: Read the following facts about the early U.S. economy. If it tended to encourage slavery, write an **S+** in the space provided. If it tended to discourage slavery, write an **S−**.

_S+_ **18. Rocky New England soil did not encourage large farms, so New England families could usually farm their own fields.**

_S−_ **19. The growing of tobacco required a great deal of care and labor.**

_S+_ **20. Many mills and factories were built in the North.**

_S−_ **21. Fertile southern soil encouraged very large farms, and the warmer southern climate had a longer growing season. Farmers could not operate such large farms by themselves.**

_S+_ **22. Slaves were the least-expensive year-round help an employer could get.**

Social Studies   History

SS5H2 **The Effects of Reconstruction**

DIRECTIONS: Choose the best answer.

1. **Which amendment to the U.S. Constitution gave citizenship to all people born in the United States?**

    (A) Thirteenth Amendment

    (B) Fourteenth Amendment

    (C) Fifteenth Amendment

    (D) Sixteenth Amendment

2. **Which amendment to the U.S. Constitution gave African-American men the right to vote?**

    (F) Thirteenth Amendment

    (G) Fourteenth Amendment

    (H) Fifteenth Amendment

    (J) Sixteenth Amendment

3. **The Thirteenth Amendment to the U.S. Constitution _____ .**

    (A) outlawed slavery

    (B) barred former Confederate leaders from holding national or state office

    (C) made poll taxes illegal in federal elections

    (D) all of the above

4. **What political party took control during Reconstruction?**

    (F) Abolitionists

    (G) Democrats

    (H) Republicans

    (J) Freedmen

5. **Northern people who moved to the South after the Civil War were called _____ .**

    (A) scalawags

    (B) freedmen

    (C) carpetbaggers

    (D) sharecroppers

6. **Laws that required African Americans to be separated from whites in public places were known as _____ .**

    (F) Jim Crow laws

    (G) black codes

    (H) grandfather clauses

    (J) integration laws

7. **Southern people who supported Republican policies during Reconstruction were called _____ by former Confederates.**

    (A) scalawags

    (B) freedmen

    (C) carpetbaggers

    (D) sharecroppers

8. **In the system known as sharecropping, a farmer _____ .**

    (F) owned the land he farmed

    (G) rented the land he farmed by paying a share of his crop to the landowner

    (H) was able to sell most of what he grew

    (J) was usually able to make a good living

STOP

Social Studies   **History**

SS5H3

America at the Turn of the Century

DIRECTIONS: Match each of the people below to the correct description.

1. _____ **Alexander Graham Bell**

2. _____ **George Washington Carver**

3. _____ **Thomas Edison**

4. _____ **Orville Wright**

a. invented the electric lightbulb

b. flew the first motorized airplane

c. invented the telephone

d. developed hundreds of products from the peanut

DIRECTIONS: Choose the best answer.

5. **Which form of communication was introduced in the nineteenth century and is still widely used in the twenty-first century?**

  Ⓐ television

  Ⓑ telephone

  Ⓒ telegraph

  Ⓓ all of the above

6. **The discoveries of George Washington Carver had the greatest impact on the economy of the _____ .**

  Ⓕ South

  Ⓖ Northeast

  Ⓗ Midwest

  Ⓙ Southwest

7. **How did the invention of the electric lightbulb change the American economy?**

  Ⓐ Automobile factories appeared in every American city.

  Ⓑ Travelers were able to move from coast to coast in a matter of hours.

  Ⓒ Businesses could more easily operate at night.

  Ⓓ all of the above

8. **The Spanish-American War was fought during the presidency of _____ .**

  Ⓕ Grover Cleveland

  Ⓖ William McKinley

  Ⓗ Theodore Roosevelt

  Ⓙ William Howard Taft

9. **At the end of the Spanish-American War, the United States acquired all of the following territories *except* _____ .**

  Ⓐ Puerto Rico

  Ⓑ Guam

  Ⓒ the Philippines

  Ⓓ Haiti

10. **Theodore Roosevelt's approach to foreign policy was known as _____ .**

  Ⓕ dollar diplomacy

  Ⓖ moral diplomacy

  Ⓗ big stick diplomacy

  Ⓙ isolationism

11. **Construction of the Panama Canal was begun during the presidency of _____ .**

  Ⓐ Grover Cleveland

  Ⓑ William McKinley

  Ⓒ Theodore Roosevelt

  Ⓓ William Howard Taft

GO ⇒

Name _____ Date _____

DIRECTIONS: Use the map below to answer questions 12–13.

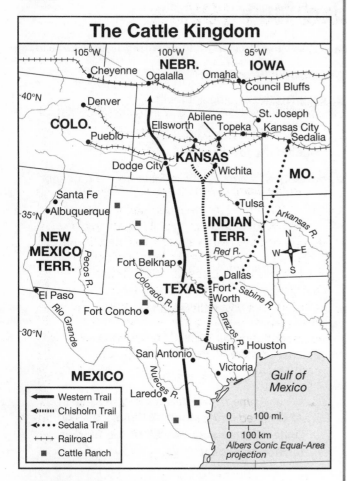

The Cattle Kingdom

DIRECTIONS: Use the chart below to answer questions 14–16.

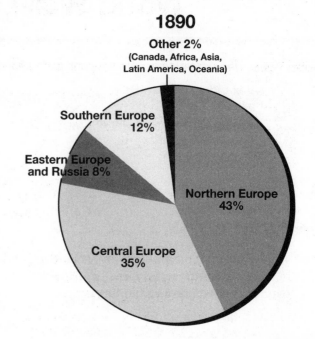

1890

12. Why did cattle trails develop?

- (F) There was not enough grass in Texas to feed the growing number of cattle.
- (G) Texas ranchers needed to get their cattle to the railroads in Kansas, Missouri, and Nebraska.
- (H) Cattle were worth much more if they could be shipped to the North and the East.
- (J) both G and H

13. Towns that were located near railroads to ship cattle were known as "cow towns." Which of the following was a cow town?

- (A) Fort Worth, Texas
- (B) Wichita, Kansas
- (C) Abilene, Kansas
- (D) St. Joseph, Missouri

14. In 1890, most immigrants to the United States came from what continent?

- (F) Africa
- (G) Asia
- (H) Europe
- (J) South America

15. Most immigrants settled in cities because _____ .

- (A) they had lived in cities in their home countries
- (B) they were able to find work in cities
- (C) they wanted to live near other immigrants from their own countries
- (D) both B and C

16. Many of the immigrants from Russia were Jewish. What is the primary reason that they came to the United States?

- (F) to escape overcrowding
- (G) to escape persecution
- (H) to escape a cholera epidemic
- (J) because of crop failures

Name _____ Date _____

SS5H4

The United States in World War I and the 1920s

DIRECTIONS: Read the passages below and then answer the questions that follow.

Wilson's Appeal for Neutrality
August 19, 1914

"The effect of the war upon the United States will depend upon what American citizens say and do. Every man who really loves America will act and speak in the true spirit of neutrality."

Wilson's Response to the Sinking of the *Lusitania*
May 13, 1915

"In view of recent acts of the German authorities in violation of American rights on the high seas which culminated [resulted] in the torpedoing and sinking of the British steamship *Lusitania* on May 7, 1915, . . . it is clearly wise and desirable that [the governments of the United States and Germany] should come to a clear and full understanding as to the grave situation which has resulted."

The Zimmerman Note
January 19, 1917

(from the German Foreign Secretary to the German Ambassador in Mexico)

"[W]e intend to begin submarine warfare unrestricted. In spite of this, it is our intention to endeavor to keep neutral the United States of America. If this attempt is not successful, we propose an alliance on the following basis with Mexico: That we shall make war together and together make peace. We shall give general financial support, and it is understood that Mexico is to reconquer the lost territory in New Mexico, Texas, and Arizona."

The Zimmerman note was intercepted and published on March 1, 1917. The United States declared war on April 8, 1917.

1. **At the beginning of World War I, President Woodrow Wilson believed that the United States should _____ .**

   (A) send troops to Europe

   (B) support Germany

   (C) support Great Britain

   (D) remain neutral ✓

2. **What actions by Germany in 1915 made Wilson rethink his position?**

   (F) invasions of other European nations

   (G) attacks on U.S. and British ships ✓

   (H) German efforts to win allies in Asia

   (J) mistreatment of Russian prisoners

3. **What action by Germany in 1917 helped bring the United States into the war?**

   (A) its attempt to get Mexico to become its ally ✓

   (B) its agreements with Russia and France

   (C) its invasion of Belgium

   (D) terrorist activity in the Americas

4. **The United States entered the war on the side of the Allied Powers, which included all of the following *except* _____ .**

   (F) Austria-Hungary

   (G) France

   (H) Great Britain

   (J) Russia

GO

Name _____ Date _____

DIRECTIONS: Match each of the following people to the subject with which they are associated.

5. _____ **Louis Armstrong**

6. _____ **Henry Ford**

7. _____ **Charles Lindbergh**

8. _____ **Babe Ruth**

a. airplane

b. automobile

c. baseball

d. jazz

DIRECTIONS: Choose the best answer.

9. **The first person to fly alone across the Atlantic Ocean was _____ .**
   - (A) Orville Wright
   - (B) Amelia Earhart
   - (C) Charles Lindbergh
   - (D) Chuck Yeager

10. **The 1920s is often referred to as the Jazz Age. Jazz has its roots in _____ .**
   - (F) classical music
   - (G) European folk music
   - (H) African music
   - (J) Native-American music

DIRECTIONS: Study the chart below and then answer question 11.

Model T Ford Production

Production Time	Selling Price
1908: one car every 728 min.	1908: $850
1913: one car every 93 min.	1916: $360
1927: one car every 24 sec.	1927: $260

11. **Henry Ford introduced the assembly line in 1913. As a result of the assembly line method, _____ .**
   - (A) the price of the Model T increased
   - (B) the price of the Model T decreased
   - (C) the number of Model T's produced per day remained the same
   - (D) the efficiency of workers producing the Model T declined

DIRECTIONS: Read the passage below and then answer question 12.

". . . It was the period when the Negro was in vogue [fashion].

"I was there. I had a swell time while it lasted. But I thought it wouldn't last long. . . . [But some people] were sure the New Negro would lead a new life from then on in green pastures of tolerance created by Countee Cullen, Ethel Waters, Claude McKay, Duke Ellington, Bojangles, and Alain Locke."

Langston Hughes,
The Big Sea, an Autobiography

12. **What well-known event of the 1920s is described in this passage?**
   - (F) Prohibition
   - (G) the Harlem Renaissance
   - (H) the lost generation
   - (J) bootlegging

Georgia Test Practice

Social Studies   **History**

SS5H5

The Great Depression and the New Deal

DIRECTIONS: Match each of the people below to the correct description.

1. _____ **Duke Ellington** C ✓

2. _____ **Herbert Hoover**

3. _____ **Margaret Mitchell** d ✓

4. _____ **Jesse Owens** e ✓

5. _____ **Franklin Roosevelt**

a. U.S. president from 1929–1933

b. U.S. president from 1933–1945

c. famous jazz pianist and composer

d. author of *Gone With the Wind*

e. African-American athlete who won four gold medals at the 1936 Olympics

DIRECTIONS: Study the chart below and then answer the questions that follow.

CAUSES		EFFECTS
• Income gap between rich and poor grows • High tariffs and war debts • Overuse of credit to make purchases • Industry and agriculture supply exceed demand • Sales fall behind • International market falters • Stock market crash; financial panic	→ Great Depression →	• Millions lose jobs; poverty is widespread • Businesses and banks close • Depression spreads to other countries • Roosevelt wins presidency • New Deal legislation enacted • Despite period of economic upturn, the Depression remains

6. **Based on the chart above, which of the following statements is true?**

   Ⓐ The Stock Market Crash of 1929 was the main cause of the Great Depression.

   Ⓑ The American economy had no effect on foreign economies.

   Ⓒ The Great Depression was a brief economic crisis.

   Ⓓ Several factors led to the Great Depression.

7. **After Roosevelt took office, Congress passed laws to deal with the Depression that were called the _____ .**

   Ⓕ Brain Trust

   Ⓖ New Deal

   Ⓗ Square Deal

   Ⓙ Roosevelt Deal

8. **During the Depression, many people lost their homes and were forced to live in shantytowns. Some people referred to these shantytowns as Hoovervilles because _____ .**

   Ⓐ President Hoover had failed to act to fight the Depression

   Ⓑ President Hoover had built the shantytowns

   Ⓒ President Hoover was a very popular president

   Ⓓ President Hoover had died in office

9. **The Dust Bowl of the 1930s was caused by _____ .**

   Ⓕ clearing of sod to plant wheat

   Ⓖ a severe drought

   Ⓗ strong prairie winds

   Ⓙ all of the above

DIRECTIONS: Study the chart below and then answer the questions that follow.

The New Deal

First New Deal Program	Initials	Founded	Purpose
Civilian Conservation Corps	CCC	1933	Provided jobs for young men to plant trees and build bridges
Tennessee Valley Authority	TVA	1933	Built dams to control flooding and to provide cheap electric power to seven Southern states; set up schools and health centers
Federal Emergency Relief Administration	FERA	1933	Gave relief to unemployed and needy
Agriculture Adjustment Administration	AAA	1933	Paid farmers not to grow certain crops
National Recovery Administration	NRA	1933	Helped set standards for production, prices, and wages
Public Works Administration	PWA	1933	Built ports, schools, and aircraft carriers
Federal Deposit Insurance Corporation	FDIC	1933	Insured savings accounts in banks approved by the government
Second New Deal Program			
Rural Electrification Administration	REA	1935	Loaned money to extend electricity to rural areas
Works Progress Administration	WPA	1935	Employed men and women to build hospitals, schools, parks, and airports; employed artists, writers, and musicians
Social Security Act	SSA	1935	Set up a system of pensions for the elderly, unemployed, and people with disabilities
Farm Security Administration	FSA	1937	Lent money to sharecroppers; set up camps for migrant workers
Fair Labor Standards Act	FLSA	1938	Established minimum wages and maximum hours for all businesses engaged in interstate commerce

10. **Which New Deal program provided monthly pensions for retired people?**
    - (A) National Recovery Administration
    - (B) Works Progress Administration
    - (C) Social Security Act
    - (D) Fair Labor Standards Act

11. **What natural disaster was prevented by a New Deal program?**
    - (F) the Dust Bowl
    - (G) flooding of the Tennessee River
    - (H) droughts in Kansas
    - (J) hurricanes in Florida

12. **Which New Deal program provided jobs for unemployed people?**
    - (A) Civilian Conservation Corps
    - (B) Works Progress Administration
    - (C) Fair Labor Standards Act
    - (D) both A and B

13. **Which New Deal program was created to prevent future banking crises?**
    - (F) Agricultural Adjustment Administration
    - (G) National Recovery Administration
    - (H) Federal Deposit Insurance Corporation
    - (J) Farm Security Administration

Social Studies   **History**

SS5H6

The United States and World War II

DIRECTIONS: Match each of the people below to the correct description.

1. _____ **Winston Churchill**

2. _____ **Hirohito**

3. _____ **Adolf Hitler**

4. _____ **Benito Mussolini**

5. _____ **Joseph Stalin**

6. _____ **Harry Truman**

a. German dictator

b. Soviet dictator

c. British prime minister

d. Japanese emperor

e. American president

f. Italian dictator

 Clue   **D-Day** is the day Allied forces began the invasion of France, **V-E Day** stands for Victory in Europe, and **V-J Day** stands for Victory over Japan.

DIRECTIONS: Choose the best answer.

7. **What event caused the United States to enter World War II?**
   - Ⓐ D-Day
   - Ⓑ bombing of Hiroshima and Nagasaki
   - Ⓒ bombing of Pearl Harbor
   - Ⓓ the Holocaust

8. **The day the Allied forces landed on the coast of Normandy, France, is called _____ .**
   - Ⓕ D-Day
   - Ⓖ V-E Day
   - Ⓗ V-J Day
   - Ⓙ Iwo Jima

9. **Germany surrendered on May 7, 1945, and the Allies called the next day _____ .**
   - Ⓐ D-Day
   - Ⓑ V-E Day
   - Ⓒ V-J Day
   - Ⓓ Allied Day

10. **Because Japan had agreed to surrender, August 15, 1945 was declared _____ .**
    - Ⓕ D-Day
    - Ⓖ V-E Day
    - Ⓗ V-J Day
    - Ⓙ none of these

11. **What action did the U.S. government take against Japanese Americans after the bombing of Pearl Harbor?**
    - Ⓐ It sent them back to Japan.
    - Ⓑ It forced them into slave labor.
    - Ⓒ It took away all their money.
    - Ⓓ It placed them in internment camps.

12. **During the war, "Rosie the Riveter" became a symbol for women who _____ .**
    - Ⓕ stayed at home
    - Ⓖ worked in defense plants
    - Ⓗ served in the military
    - Ⓙ had lost their husbands in the war

GO

Name _____ Date _____

DIRECTIONS: Study the map below and then answer the questions that follow.

Lands Conquered by Nazi Germany, 1936–1939

North Sea

Baltic Sea

POLAND
September 1939

GERMANY

RHINELAND
1936

CZECHOSLOVAKIA
March 1939

SUDETENLAND
September 1938

AUSTRIA
March 1938

13. What land was conquered by the Nazis first?

- (A) Poland
- (B) Austria
- (C) Rhineland
- (D) Sudetenland

14. In March 1938, Hitler sent troops into _____ and annexed it.

- (F) Poland
- (G) Austria
- (H) Rhineland
- (J) Sudetenland

15. At the Munich Conference in September 1938, European leaders decided to satisfy Hitler by turning _____ over to him.

- (A) Poland
- (B) Austria
- (C) Rhineland
- (D) Sudetenland

16. After signing the Soviet-German Non-Aggression Pact in August 1939, Hitler sent his armies into _____ .

- (F) Poland
- (G) Austria
- (H) Rhineland
- (J) Sudetenland

17. The alliance of Germany, Italy, and _____ made up what was known as the Axis Powers.

- (A) Great Britain
- (B) France
- (C) Japan
- (D) Soviet Union

18. The mass slaughter of Jews and other groups by the Nazis during World War II is known as _____ .

- (F) the Bataan Death March
- (G) the Holocaust
- (H) Operation Overlord
- (J) the Great Internment

Georgia Test Practice

Name _____ Date _____

SS5H7

The Cold War

DIRECTIONS: Study the chart below and then answer the questions that follow.

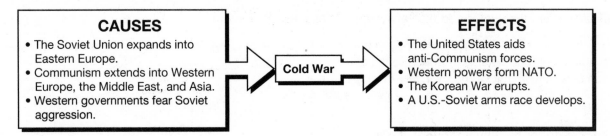

CAUSES
- The Soviet Union expands into Eastern Europe.
- Communism extends into Western Europe, the Middle East, and Asia.
- Western governments fear Soviet aggression.

Cold War

EFFECTS
- The United States aids anti-Communism forces.
- Western powers form NATO.
- The Korean War erupts.
- A U.S.-Soviet arms race develops.

1. **The Cold War between the United States and the former Soviet Union was a rivalry between what two forms of government?**
   - (A) communism and socialism
   - (B) communism and dictatorship
   - (C) communism and democracy
   - (D) democracy and monarchy

2. **What event caused Truman to send American troops to Korea in 1950?**
   - (F) the invasion of South Korea by North Korea
   - (G) the invasion of North Korea by South Korea
   - (H) the Communist revolution in China
   - (J) the defeat of the French in Vietnam

3. **In a speech in 1946, Winston Churchill declared that an "iron curtain" had descended across Europe. What did Churchill mean by the "iron curtain"?**
   - (A) the wall separating East and West Berlin
   - (B) the separation of the Communist countries in Eastern Europe from the democratic nations in the West
   - (C) the division of Germany agreed upon at the Yalta Conference
   - (D) the railroad system in Eastern Europe

4. **Americans' fear of communism following World War II led to all of the following except _____ .**
   - (F) blacklists
   - (G) the execution of the Rosenbergs
   - (H) a hunt for Communists by Senator Joseph McCarthy
   - (J) greater tolerance of people with radical ideas

5. **The two military alliances that opposed each other in Europe during the Cold War were the Warsaw Pact and the _____ .**
   - (A) Axis Powers
   - (B) League of Nations
   - (C) North Atlantic Treaty Organization (NATO)
   - (D) Southeast Asia Treaty Organization (SEATO)

6. **In response to the Soviet blockade of West Berlin in 1948, the United States and Great Britain _____ .**
   - (F) sent troops to end the blockade
   - (G) built the Berlin Wall
   - (H) organized an airlift to supply the city
   - (J) blockaded Moscow

STOP

Social Studies   **History**

SS5H8

People and Events
from 1950–1975

DIRECTIONS: Read the quotes and then answer the questions that follow.

"You have a row of dominoes set up, you knock over the first one, and what will happen to the last one is the certainty that it will go over very quickly . . ."

Dwight Eisenhower

1. **According to the domino theory, if one country in Southeast Asia fell to communism, the other countries in the area would also fall. This theory led the United States to enter what war?**

    (A) World War II

    (B) Korean War

    (C) Vietnam War

    (D) Persian Gulf War

"Now let us say that we are not advocating [supporting] violence . . . The only weapon we have in our hands this evening is the weapon of protest."

Martin Luther King, Jr.

2. **Martin Luther King, Jr., encouraged his followers to _____ .**

    (F) use violence

    (G) obey laws even when the laws were unjust

    (H) fight back when attacked

    (J) use nonviolent protest

"In a land of great wealth, families must not live in hopeless poverty . . . In a great land of learning and scholars, young people must be taught to read and write."

Lyndon B. Johnson

3. **President Johnson called his social programs the _____ .**

    (A) New Deal

    (B) Square Deal

    (C) New Frontier

    (D) Great Society

DIRECTIONS: Choose the best answer.

4. **What event in the 1960s brought the world close to nuclear war?**

    (F) the Bay of Pigs invasion

    (G) construction of the Berlin Wall

    (H) the Cuban Missile Crisis

    (J) the Apollo project

5. **What Supreme Court case in 1954 led to the desegregation of schools?**

    (A) *Plessy v. Ferguson*

    (B) *Norris v. Alabama*

    (C) *Brown v. Board of Education*

    (D) *Sweatt v. Painter*

6. **What agency was created after the Soviets launched the satellite *Sputnik*?**

    (F) National Aeronautics and Space Administration

    (G) Central Intelligence Agency

    (H) Federal Bureau of Investigation

    (J) House Un-American Activities Committee

GO

7. **Which person's arrest led African Americans to organize the Montgomery bus boycott?**

   (A) Medgar Evers

   (B) Rosa Parks

   (C) Malcolm X

   (D) Thurgood Marshall

8. **Which of the following finally gave all citizens equal access to restaurants, hotels, libraries, and theaters?**

   (F) the Civil Rights Act of 1964

   (G) the Voting Rights Act of 1965

   (H) the Twenty-Fourth Amendment

   (J) the Equal Rights Amendment

DIRECTIONS: Answer the questions below. Use the Internet or library resources to help you if necessary.

9. **By the end of the 1950s, most American families owned television sets. How did television change American life?**

   _____

   _____

   _____

   _____

   _____

   _____

   _____

   _____

   _____

   _____

   _____

   _____

   _____

10. **John F. Kennedy, Robert F. Kennedy, and Martin Luther King, Jr., were all assassinated in the 1960s. What impact did their assassinations have on American society?**

    _____

    _____

    _____

    _____

    _____

    _____

    _____

    _____

    _____

    _____

    _____

    _____

    _____

    _____

    _____

    _____

STOP

Social Studies   History

SS5H9 # Developments Since 1975

DIRECTIONS: Choose the best answer.

1. **In 1978, President Jimmy Carter helped negotiate a peace agreement, known as the Camp David Accords, between Egypt and _____ .**

   (A) the Palestine Liberation Organization

   (B) Israel

   (C) the Soviet Union

   (D) the United States

2. **The Iraqi invasion of Kuwait in 1990 resulted in the _____ .**

   (F) fall of the government of Saddam Hussein

   (G) Iran-Iraq War

   (H) Persian Gulf War

   (J) War on Terrorism

3. **How did Presidents Reagan and Bush help bring about the end of the Cold War?**

   (A) They signed agreements with the Soviet Union to end the arms race.

   (B) They supported uprisings in the Soviet republics.

   (C) They sent troops to tear down the Berlin Wall.

   (D) They supported the Sandinistas in Nicaragua.

4. **The democratic movement in Eastern Europe in the 1980s began in _____ .**

   (F) the Soviet Union

   (G) Poland

   (H) Germany

   (J) Czechoslovakia

5. **The last president of the Soviet Union was _____ .**

   (A) Mikhail Gorbachev

   (B) Boris Yeltsin

   (C) Leonid Brezhnev

   (D) Nikita Khrushchev

6. **The War on Terrorism began in response to _____ .**

   (F) ethnic cleansing in Bosnia

   (G) the Soviet invasion of Afghanistan

   (H) Saddam Hussein's refusal to give up weapons of mass destruction

   (J) attacks in the United States on September 11, 2001

7. **The development of the microchip led to _____ .**

   (A) the invention of the computer

   (B) an increase in the size of computers

   (C) the development of the personal computer

   (D) a decrease in the use of computers

8. **What impact has the development of the personal computer and the Internet had on American life?**

   _____

   _____

   _____

   _____

   _____

   _____

   _____

   _____

STOP

Social Studies   History

SS5H1–SS5H9

Mini-Test 1

For pages 128–142

DIRECTIONS: Choose the best answer.

1. **Which of the following statements about the South before the Civil War is true?**

   Ⓐ There were many mills and factories in the South.

   Ⓑ Few Southerners made their living by farming.

   Ⓒ With the help of their families, Southern farmers could farm their own land.

   Ⓓ Southern farmers used slaves to help them farm their large plantations.

2. **Who surrendered to General Grant at Appomattox Court House?**

   Ⓕ Robert E. Lee

   Ⓖ Thomas "Stonewall" Jackson

   Ⓗ William Tecumseh Sherman

   Ⓙ Jefferson Davis

3. **Which amendment to the U.S. Constitution outlawed slavery?**

   Ⓐ Thirteenth Amendment

   Ⓑ Fourteenth Amendment

   Ⓒ Fifteenth Amendment

   Ⓓ Sixteenth Amendment

4. **Which of the following events took place during the presidency of Theodore Roosevelt?**

   Ⓕ the Spanish-American War

   Ⓖ the acquisition of the Philippines

   Ⓗ the construction of the Panama Canal

   Ⓙ all of the above

5. **What actions by Germany led the United States to enter World War I?**

   Ⓐ attacks on U.S. ships

   Ⓑ sinking of the *Lusitania*

   Ⓒ the Zimmerman note

   Ⓓ all of the above

6. **Most New Deal legislation was designed to _____ .**

   Ⓕ reform the federal government

   Ⓖ improve relations with other countries

   Ⓗ deal with the nation's economic problems

   Ⓙ advance civil rights

7. **Before the bombing of Pearl Harbor, the United States _____ .**

   Ⓐ sent troops to help the Allies

   Ⓑ sent troops to help the Axis Powers

   Ⓒ supplied arms to Great Britain

   Ⓓ supported Japanese expansion in Asia

8. **The Cold War was primarily a rivalry between the United States and _____ .**

   Ⓕ the Soviet Union

   Ⓖ Great Britain

   Ⓗ Germany

   Ⓙ Japan

9. **The United States sent troops to Vietnam _____ .**

   Ⓐ because of Americans' concern for civil rights

   Ⓑ to stop the spread of communism

   Ⓒ as a result of the Cuban Missile Crisis

   Ⓓ to help defeat the French

10. **The Persian Gulf War began as a result of _____ .**

   Ⓕ the attacks on September 11, 2001

   Ⓖ the breakup of the Soviet Union

   Ⓗ the Iraqi invasion of Kuwait

   Ⓙ democratic reform in Eastern Europe

STOP

Geography Standards

SS5G1. The student will locate important places in the United States.
(See pages 145–146.)
a. Locate important physical features, including the Grand Canyon, Salton Sea, Great Salt Lake, and the Mojave Desert.
b. Locate important man-made places, including the Chisholm Trail; Pittsburgh, PA; Gettysburg, PA; Kitty Hawk, NC; Pearl Harbor, HI; and Montgomery, AL.

SS5G2. The student will explain the reasons for the spatial patterns of economic activities. *(See pages 147–148.)*
a. Identify and explain the factors influencing industrial location in the United States after the Civil War.
b. Define, map, and explain the dispersion of the primary economic activities within the United States since the turn of the century.
c. Map and explain how the dispersion of global economic activities contributed to the United States emerging from World War I as a world power.

Name _____   Date _____

SS5G1

Locating Physical Features
of the United States

DIRECTIONS: Match the letters on the map with the places listed below.

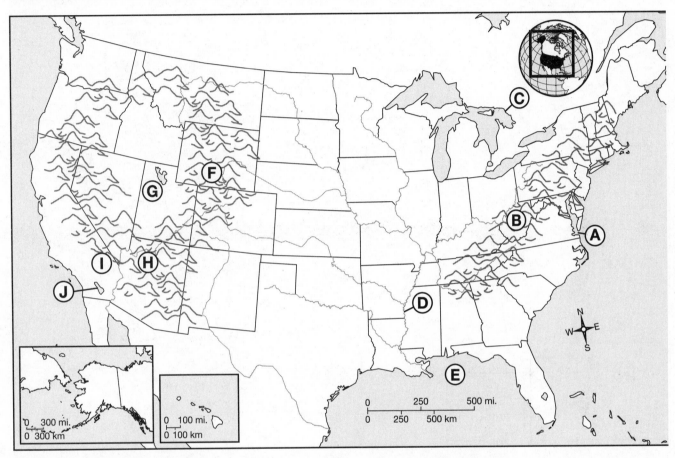

_____ 1. **Appalachian Mountains**   _____ 6. **Gulf of Mexico**

_____ 2. **Chesapeake Bay**   _____ 7. **Mississippi River**

_____ 3. **Grand Canyon**   _____ 8. **Mojave Desert**

_____ 4. **Great Lakes**   _____ 9. **Rocky Mountains**

_____ 5. **Great Salt Lake**   _____ 10. **Salton Sea**

STOP

Social Studies

SS5G1

Locating Important Places in the United States

Geography

DIRECTIONS: Match the letters on the map with the places listed below.

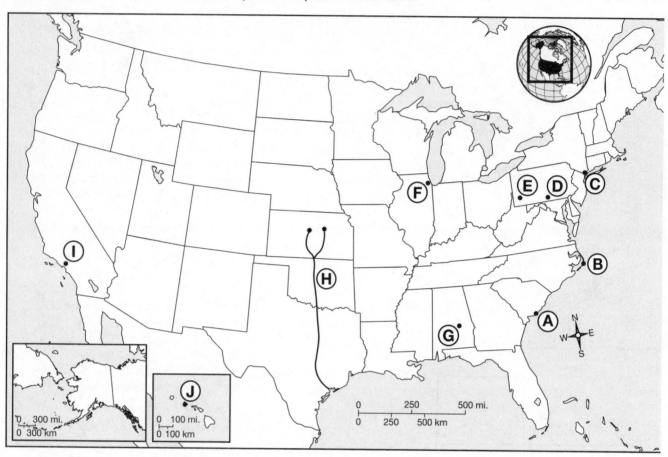

_____ 1. New York, New York

_____ 2. Chisholm Trail

_____ 3. Fort Sumter, South Carolina

_____ 4. Gettysburg, Pennsylvania

_____ 5. Kitty Hawk, North Carolina

_____ 6. Montgomery, Alabama

_____ 7. Los Angeles, California

_____ 8. Pearl Harbor, Hawaii

_____ 9. Pittsburgh, Pennsylvania

_____ 10. Chicago, Illinois

STOP

Georgia Test Practice

Name _____ Date _____

Social Studies   **Geography**

Factors Affecting Industrial Location in the United States

DIRECTIONS: Read the passage below and then choose the best answers.

The period from the end of the Civil War to 1900 was an era of unmatched economic growth in the United States. New methods in technology and business allowed the country to tap its rich supply of natural resources, increase its production, and raise the money needed for growth. The change from an agricultural economy to an industrial one was possible because the United States had the resources needed for a growing economy. Among these resources were what economists call the factors of production: land, labor, and capital.

The first factor of production, **land,** means not just the land itself but all natural resources. The second factor of production is **labor.** Large numbers of workers were needed to turn raw materials into goods. The third production factor, **capital,** is the buildings, machinery, and tools used in production. The term "capital" is also used to mean money available for investment.

The oil industry grew rapidly in the late 1800s, after oil was discovered in western Pennsylvania. Steel also became a huge business at this time. In the 1870s, large steel mills were built close to sources of iron ore in western Pennsylvania and eastern Ohio. Pittsburgh, Pennsylvania, became the steel capital of the United States. Cities located near the mines and close to waterways, like Cleveland, Chicago, Detroit, and Birmingham, Alabama, also became centers of steel production.

Some of the strongest industrial advances in the South were in the textile industry. Before the Civil War, Southern planters had shipped cotton to textile mills in the North or in Europe. In the 1880s, textile mills sprang up throughout the South. Many Northern mills began to close as companies built new plants in the South. A cheap and reliable workforce helped Southern industry grow. A railroad building boom also aided industrial growth in the South. Still, the South did not develop an industrial economy as strong as the North's. The South remained primarily agricultural.

1. The three factors of production are land, labor, and _____ .

   Ⓐ natural resources

   Ⓑ technology

   Ⓒ industry

   Ⓓ capital

2. What two industries developed in western Pennsylvania in the late 1800s?

   Ⓕ oil and steel

   Ⓖ oil and textile

   Ⓗ steel and textile

   Ⓙ textile and agriculture

3. What industry shifted from the North to the South in the late 1800s?

   Ⓐ the oil industry

   Ⓑ the steel industry

   Ⓒ the textile industry

   Ⓓ the agricultural industry

4. Besides the railroad building boom, what helped Southern industry grow?

   Ⓕ the discovery of oil

   Ⓖ the workforce in the South

   Ⓗ a lack of agriculture in the South

   Ⓙ a lack of industry in the North

Social Studies   **Geography**

SS5G2 # Mapping Economic Activities
in the United States

DIRECTIONS: Study the map below and then answer the questions that follow.

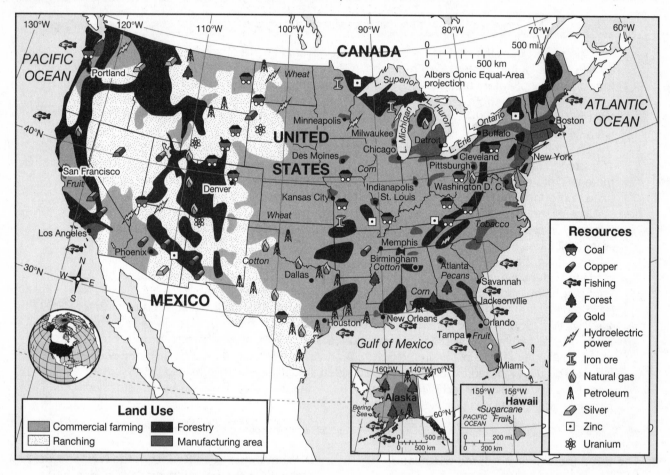

1. **Based on the map, what is the primary use of land in Iowa?**

   (A) commercial farming

   (B) forestry

   (C) manufacturing

   (D) ranching

2. **Based on the map, where is most of the manufacturing in Georgia located?**

   (F) in the southern part of the state

   (G) along the Atlantic coast

   (H) in the Atlanta area

   (J) There is no manufacturing in Georgia.

3. **Which of the following is *not* a significant economic activity in Texas?**

   (A) ranching

   (B) cotton farming

   (C) oil and gas production

   (D) gold mining

4. **Which of the following resources do California, Maine, and Florida have in common?**

   (F) gold

   (G) coal

   (H) fish

   (J) uranium

Social Studies   Geography

SS5G1–SS5G2

Mini-Test 2

For pages 145–148

DIRECTIONS: Study the map below and then answer the questions that follow.

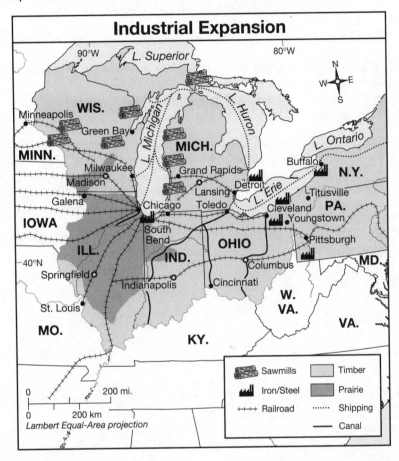

Industrial Expansion

1. **Which of the following cities was a center of the steel industry?**

   (A) St. Louis, Missouri

   (B) Indianapolis, Indiana

   (C) Cincinnati, Ohio

   (D) Pittsburgh, Pennsylvania ✓

2. **Why did the steel industry thrive in eastern Ohio and western Pennsylvania?**

   (F) Oil was discovered in the area.

   (G) Iron ore was mined in the area. ✓

   (H) There was no other industry in the area.

   (J) Work in the steel mills was safe and easy.

3. **Many sawmills were located in Wisconsin and Michigan because these two states had**

   _____ .

   (A) iron ore

   (B) petroleum

   (C) timber ✓

   (D) gold

4. **What did Chicago, Detroit, and Cleveland have in common?**

   (F) They were all located in the same state.

   (G) They were all located on the Great Lakes.

   (H) They were all centers of steel production.

   (J) both G and H ✓

STOP

Government/Civics Standards

SS5CG1. The student will explain how a citizen's rights are protected under the U.S. Constitution. *(See pages 151–152.)*
a. Explain the responsibilities of a citizen.
b. Explain the freedoms granted by the Bill of Rights.
c. Explain the concept of due process of law.
d. Describe how the Constitution protects a citizen's rights by due process.

SS5CG2. The student will explain the process by which amendments to the U.S. Constitution are made. *(See page 153.)*
a. Explain the amendment process outlined in the Constitution.
b. Describe the purpose for the amendment process.

SS5CG3. The student will explain how amendments to the U.S. Constitution have maintained a representative democracy. *(See page 153.)*
a. Explain the purpose of the Twelfth and Seventeenth Amendments.
b. Explain how voting rights were protected by the Fifteenth, Nineteenth, Twenty-Third, Twenty-Fourth, and Twenty-Sixth Amendments.

SS5CG4. The student will explain the meaning of and reason for the motto of the United States, *"E pluribus unum."* (See page 154.)

Social Studies

SS5CG1

Rights and Responsibilities of Citizens

DIRECTIONS: Choose the best answer.

1. **Every right has a responsibility that goes with it. For example, as Americans, we have the right to free speech. But this right means that we must also be sure _____ .**

   (A) never to criticize the government

   (B) to write to the president at least once every year

   ✓ (C) that the things we say are accurate and truthful

   (D) to silence any viewpoint we disagree with

2. **To be a responsible citizen, all Americans should _____ .**

   (F) obey the law

   (G) stay informed about current events

   (H) vote

   ✓ (J) all of the above

3. **In the United States, every citizen over the age of 18 has the right to vote. What are some responsibilities citizens have when it comes to voting? Explain your answer.**

   _____

   _____

   _____

   _____

   _____

   _____

4. **In the United States, if you are accused of a crime and cannot afford to hire a lawyer, the government will provide a lawyer for you. How does this benefit the accused person?**

   By ensuring that the accused receives a fair trial

   _____

   _____

   _____

5. **The U.S. Constitution guarantees the following rights to all U.S. citizens. Place a 1 beside the right you think is most important, a 2 beside the right you think is next important, and so on. Then briefly explain your rankings.**

   _____ the right to keep and bear arms

   _____ the right to a speedy and public trial

   _____ the right to vote

   __1__ the right to practice their religion

   _____

   _____

   _____

   _____

   _____

STOP

The Bill of Rights and Due Process of Law

DIRECTIONS: Choose the best answer.

1. **The first ten amendments to the U.S. Constitution are called the _____ .**
   - (A) Preamble
   - (B) Articles
   - ✓(C) Bill of Rights
   - (D) Civil War amendments

2. **The First Amendment guarantees all of the following *except* _____ .**
   - (F) freedom of speech
   - (G) freedom of assembly
   - (H) freedom of the press
   - ✓(J) the right to bear arms

3. **If you are accused of a crime, which of the following guarantees you a speedy and public trial?**
   - (A) First Amendment
   - (B) Second Amendment
   - (C) Fourth Amendment
   - ✓(D) Sixth Amendment

4. **The Fourth Amendment guarantees that you and your property cannot be searched without a warrant. A warrant is _____ .**
   - ✓(F) an order from a judge
   - (G) an order from the president
   - (H) a ticket from a policeman
   - (J) the same as bail money

5. **Which amendment guarantees freedom of religion?**
   - ✓(A) First Amendment
   - (B) Second Amendment
   - (C) Fifth Amendment
   - (D) Sixth Amendment

6. **The Ninth Amendment says _____ .**
   - (F) that the only rights a person has are those listed in the Bill of Rights
   - (G) that people have only 10 rights
   - (H) that the Bill of Rights does not list all the rights a person has
   - (J) nothing about people's rights

DIRECTIONS: Read the quotes below and then answer the questions that follow.

"You have the right to remain silent. Anything you say can be used against you in a court of law. You have the right to an attorney present now and during any future questioning. If you cannot afford an attorney, one will be appointed to you free of charge if you wish."

7. **People who are in police custody must be told their rights to ensure that they do not unknowingly incriminate, or provide evidence against, themselves. This protection is guaranteed by the _____ .**
   - (A) First Amendment
   - (B) Fourth Amendment
   - (C) Fifth Amendment
   - (D) Tenth Amendment

"No person shall be . . . deprived of life, liberty, or property, without due process of law . . ."

8. **"Due process" means that _____ .**
   - (F) a person's rights to life, liberty, and property can never be taken away
   - (G) a person's rights cannot be taken away without a fair trial and equal protection
   - (H) people must pay dues to keep their rights
   - (J) people cannot be forced to pay taxes

STOP

SS5CG2–SS5CG3

Amendments to the Constitution

DIRECTIONS: Study the chart below and then answer the questions that follow.

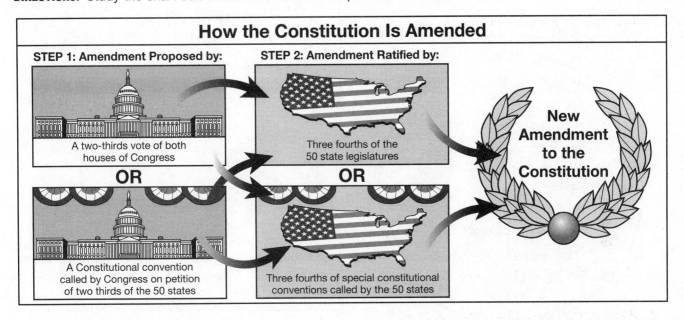

How the Constitution Is Amended

STEP 1: Amendment Proposed by:

A two-thirds vote of both houses of Congress

OR

A Constitutional convention called by Congress on petition of two thirds of the 50 states

STEP 2: Amendment Ratified by:

Three fourths of the 50 state legislatures

OR

Three fourths of special constitutional conventions called by the 50 states

New Amendment to the Constitution

---

1. Amendments to the U.S. Constitution must be ratified, or approved, by _____ .
   - Ⓐ a two-thirds vote of both houses of Congress
   - Ⓑ three-fourths of the state legislatures
   - Ⓒ three-fourths of the state constitutional conventions
   - Ⓓ either B or C

2. The Twenty-Sixth Amendment gave the right to vote to _____ .
   - Ⓕ African Americans
   - Ⓖ women
   - Ⓗ citizens of Washington, D.C.
   - Ⓙ citizens eighteen years of age or older

3. Women received the right to vote in national elections as the result of the _____ .
   - Ⓐ Fifteenth Amendment
   - Ⓑ Nineteenth Amendment
   - Ⓒ Equal Rights Amendment
   - Ⓓ Voting Rights Act of 1965

4. The Seventeenth Amendment provides that _____ .
   - Ⓕ people, not state legislatures, will elect senators
   - Ⓖ the legislatures of each state will choose senators
   - Ⓗ senators will be appointed by the president
   - Ⓙ senators can serve only two terms in office

STOP

SS5CG4

E Pluribus Unum

DIRECTIONS: Study the picture of the Great Seal of the United States below. Then answer the questions that follow.

Great Seal of the United States

1. **The Great Seal has the motto *E pluribus unum*. What does *E pluribus unum* mean?**

   (A)   Out of many, one.

   (B)   Out of one, many.

   (C)   One is the same as many.

   (D)   none of the above

2. **This motto refers to _____ .**

   (F)   the separation of powers in government

   (G)   the creation of one nation from 13 colonies

   (H)   the right of states to secede from the union

   (J)   all of the above

DIRECTIONS: Study the pie chart below and then answer the question that follows.

Foreign-Born Population in the United States: 2003

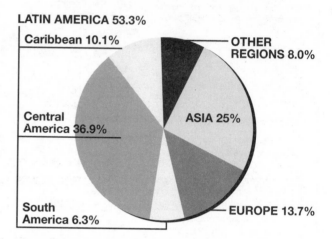

LATIN AMERICA 53.3%

Caribbean 10.1%

OTHER REGIONS 8.0%

Central America 36.9%

ASIA 25%

South America 6.3%

EUROPE 13.7%

Source: U.S. Census Bureau, Current Population Survey, 2003 Annual Social and Economic Supplement.

3. **Over time, the motto *E pluribus unum* has also come to mean something else, which is illustrated by the pie chart above. Based on the pie chart, what is another meaning for this motto?**

   (A)   All Americans are the same.

   (B)   There are too many people in the United States.

   (C)   The United States is one nation of people from many different backgrounds.

   (D)   all of the above

STOP

Social Studies

SS5CG1–SS5CG4

For pages 151–154

Government/Civics

Mini-Test 3

DIRECTIONS: Choose the best answer.

1. In order to vote in the United States, a citizen must _____ .
   - (A) be 18 years of age or older ✓
   - (B) be 21 years of age or older
   - (C) pay a poll tax
   - (D) pass a test

2. Which of the following statements about amendments to the Constitution is true?
   - (F) If an amendment is proposed by a two-thirds vote of Congress, it does not need to be approved by the states.
   - (G) Only state legislatures can approve amendments.
   - (H) Only Congress can propose amendments.
   - (J) Amendments can be repealed. ✓

3. The First Amendment does *not* give you the right to _____ .
   - (A) choose your own religion
   - (B) print your ideas
   - (C) make speeches
   - (D) cry "fire" in a movie theater ✓

4. The motto *E pluribus unum* means that _____ .
   - (F) the United States has a strong economy
   - (G) the United States has a diverse population
   - (H) the United States is one nation made up of several states
   - (J) both G and H ✓

5. The Fifteenth Amendment gave the right to vote to _____ .
   - (A) former male slaves ✓
   - (B) women
   - (C) citizens of Washington, D.C.
   - (D) citizens 18 years of age or older

6. The Bill of Rights is the _____ amendments to the Constitution.
   - (F) first five
   - (G) first 10 ✓
   - (H) first 12
   - (J) entire 27

7. If your house is searched without a warrant, this is a violation of your _____ rights.
   - (A) First Amendment
   - (B) Second Amendment
   - (C) Fourth Amendment ✓
   - (D) Fifth Amendment

8. When people say that they want to "plead the Fifth," this means that they _____ .
   - (F) want to exercise free speech
   - (G) want to choose their religion
   - (H) want a trial
   - (J) choose to remain silent so that they will not incriminate themselves ✓

9. "Due process of law" protects a person's rights to _____ .
   - (A) life
   - (B) liberty
   - (C) property
   - (D) all of the above ✓

STOP

Economics Standards

SS5E1. The student will use the basic economic concepts of *trade, opportunity cost, specialization, voluntary exchange, productivity,* and *price incentives* to illustrate historical events. *(See pages 157–159.)*

a. Describe *opportunity costs* and their relationship to decision-making across time (such as decisions to remain unengaged at the beginning of World War II in Europe).

b. Explain how *price incentives* affect people's behavior and choices (such as monetary policy during the Great Depression).

c. Describe how *specialization* improves standards of living (such as how development of specific economies in the North and South developed at the beginning of the twentieth century).

d. Explain how *voluntary exchange* helps both buyers and sellers (such as the G8 countries).

e. Describe how *trade* promotes economic activity (such as trade activities today under NAFTA).

f. Give examples of technological advancements and their impact on business during the development of the United States.

SS5E2. The student will describe the functions of the three major institutions in the U.S. economy in each era of United States history. *(See pages 160–161.)*

a. Describe the *private business function* in producing goods and services.

b. Describe the *bank function* in providing checking accounts, savings accounts, and loans.

c. Describe the *government function* in taxation and providing certain goods and services.

SS5E3. The student will describe how *consumers* and *businesses* interact in the U.S. economy across time. *(See pages 162–164.)*

a. Describe how *competition, markets,* and *prices* influence people's behavior.

b. Describe how people earn *income* by selling their labor to businesses.

c. Describe how *entrepreneurs* take risks to develop new goods and services to start a business.

SS5E4. The student will identify the elements of a *personal budget* and explain why personal *spending* and *saving* decisions are important. *(See pages 165–166.)*

Name _____ Date _____

Opportunity Costs

DIRECTIONS: Read the story and then answer the questions.

> Jenny has $20 to spend. She would like to have the latest Biggie Boys CD, which costs $17. She'd also like to go out for pizza and a movie with her friends Maria and Chantel. She figures that would cost about $15. Then again, her brother's birthday is next week. Jenny knows he's a fan of those Wally Wizard books. She could surprise him with the newest book for $19.50. Of course, she really should repay her dad for that $10 she borrowed a few days ago. And for just $7.50, she could refill her secret supply of Choco-Nut bars she keeps hidden in her room. All the way home from school, Jenny thought and thought about what to do with that money.

Clue   **Opportunity cost** is the next best alternative that is given up when a choice is made.

1. **Suppose Jenny decides to repay the $10 she borrowed from her dad. In that case, she will have to give up _____ .**

   Ⓐ going out for pizza and a movie with her friends

   Ⓑ refilling her secret supply of Choco-Nut bars

   Ⓒ buying the Biggie Boys CD

   Ⓓ both A and C

2. **After thinking it over, Jenny decides to rank her choices: her first choice is buying a Wally Wizard book for her brother, second is buying the Biggie Boys CD, third is repaying her dad, fourth is going out for pizza and a movie with her friends, and fifth is refilling her secret supply of Choco-Nut bars. Her opportunity cost is the item that is ranked second on her list. In this case, Jenny's opportunity cost is _____ .**

   Ⓕ buying the Biggie Boys CD

   Ⓖ repaying her dad and refilling her supply of Choco-Nut bars

   Ⓗ buying the Wally Wizard book

   Ⓙ all of the other choices are Jenny's opportunity cost

3. **Which of the following actions could Jenny take to get rid of her opportunity cost?**

   Ⓐ She could buy the Biggie Boys CD after all.

   Ⓑ She could go out with her friends but buy their pizza for them.

   Ⓒ She could put the money in the bank instead of spending it.

   Ⓓ None of the above. In each case, Jenny is giving something up.

4. **Which of the following was an opportunity cost for the United States when the decision was made to enter World War II?**

   Ⓕ Automakers had to stop building cars to produce trucks and tanks.

   Ⓖ Consumer goods, such as shoes, tires, and sugar, were needed for the war effort and had to be rationed.

   Ⓗ Millions of American workers left their jobs and joined the armed forces.

   Ⓙ all of the above

Social Studies

SS5E1

Specialization and Productivity

DIRECTIONS: Choose the best answer.

1. When the production of a good is broken down into several separate tasks, with different workers performing each task, it is called _____ .

   (A) productivity

   ✓ (B) division of labor

   (C) entrepreneurship

   (D) unemployment

2. Building a car is a complicated job. The fastest way to build a car is _____ .

   ✓ (F) for many people to do one part of the job and become very good at it

   (G) for one person to build the car all alone

   (H) both F and G would be equally fast

   (J) F would be faster at first, but after a while G would be faster

DIRECTIONS: When workers are specialized, they have particular skills that they use to do their jobs. Specialization on the job has both good points and bad points. Write a **B** beside each condition if you think it is a benefit of specialization. Write a **D** if you think it is a disadvantage of specialization.

_b_ 3. Over time, specialized workers become very good at what they do.

_d_ 4. Production can slow down if a specialized worker is out sick.

_b_ 5. Specialized workers make fewer mistakes.

_d_ 6. Specialized workers may become bored performing the same task every day.

_d b_ 7. It takes less time to train a worker to do one or two tasks than to do many tasks.

8. At the Well-Built Bicycle Company, each bicycle is built completely by one person. At the Speedy Bicycle Company, a team of 15 specialized employees builds each bicycle. Each member of the team does a little bit of the work. Which company do you think builds more bicycles in a typical week? Explain your answer.

_____

_____

_____

_____

DIRECTIONS: Study the chart below and then answer the question that follows.

┌───┐
| **Production Time for the Model T Ford** |
| 1908: one car every 728 minutes |
| 1913: one car every 93 minutes |
| 1927: one car every 24 seconds |
└───┘

9. Henry Ford introduced the assembly line method of production in 1913. What was the effect on production time for the Model T?

   (A) Production time increased.

   (B) Production time decreased slightly.

   ✓ (C) Production time decreased dramatically.

   (D) There was no effect on production time.

STOP

Name _____ Date _____

SS5E1

Voluntary Exchange and Trade

DIRECTIONS: Choose the best answer.

1. Trading goods and services with people for other goods and services or money is called _____ .

   (A) division of labor

   (B) extortion

   (C) exchange

   (D) scarcity

2. When two people or countries trade voluntarily, _____ .

   (F) they each have something the other one wants

   (G) they should both think they are better off after the trade than before the trade

   (H) no one forces them to make the trade

   (J) all of the above

DIRECTIONS: Examine the table below and then answer the questions.

Name of Country	Available Resources	Needed Resources
Erehwon	bananas, coffee, coal	wheat
Utopia	coal	rice
Mythos	wheat, rice	oil
Freedonia	wheat, coffee, rice	bananas

3. Based on the information in the table, with which country is Freedonia most likely to trade?

   (A) Erehwon

   (B) Utopia

   (C) Mythos

   (D) Freedonia is not likely to trade with any of the other countries.

4. Based on the information in the table, with which country is Utopia least likely to trade?

   (F) Erehwon

   (G) Freedonia

   (H) Mythos

   (J) Utopia is likely to trade with all of the other countries.

5. Mythos might be unwilling to trade with any of the other countries listed because _____ .

   (A) Mythos has all the resources it needs

   (B) none of them want the resources Mythos has to offer

   (C) none of them have the oil Mythos needs

   (D) no one in Mythos likes bananas

6. One way for Erehwon to get the resources it needs would be to _____ .

   (F) buy it from Mythos

   (G) trade bananas with Freedonia for it

   (H) buy it from Freedonia

   (J) all of the above

7. In 1994, the United States joined Mexico and Canada in the North American Free Trade Agreement (NAFTA). This agreement removed trade barriers among the three nations. Why did the United States decide to sign this treaty?

   (A) to lower prices for American consumers

   (B) to expand markets for American goods

   (C) to give jobs to Mexican workers

   (D) both A and B

STOP

Social Studies   **Economics**

SS5E2

Banks and Private Business

DIRECTIONS: Study the flowchart below. Then answer the questions that follow.

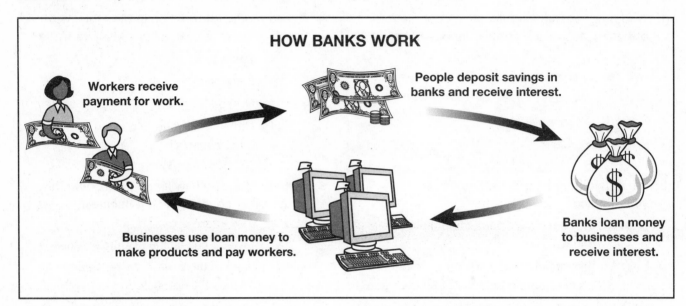

HOW BANKS WORK

Workers receive payment for work.

People deposit savings in banks and receive interest.

Businesses use loan money to make products and pay workers.

Banks loan money to businesses and receive interest.

---

1. **Why do people deposit money in savings accounts in banks?**

   Ⓐ to receive payment for work

   Ⓑ to make products

   Ⓒ to pay workers

   Ⓓ to receive interest

2. **Why do businesses borrow money?**

   Ⓕ to receive interest

   Ⓖ to make products

   Ⓗ to pay workers

   Ⓙ both G and H

3. **Why do banks loan money?**

   Ⓐ to receive interest

   Ⓑ to make products

   Ⓒ to pay workers

   Ⓓ both B and C

4. **Marcus manages an automobile factory. If he lives in a country that has a market economy, he will determine how many cars he should build this month by _____ .**

   Ⓕ asking the factory employees

   Ⓖ examining the sales figures for the company

   Ⓗ flipping a coin

   Ⓙ none of the above

5. **Suppose you ran a thing-a-ma-bob factory. As the producer, at what price would you be most likely to produce the greatest number of thing-a-ma-bobs?**

   Ⓐ $1.00

   Ⓑ $2.50

   Ⓒ $5.00

   Ⓓ the same number no matter what the price

STOP

SS5E2

Public Goods and Services

DIRECTIONS: Choose the best answer.

1. **Which of the following is *not* a reason why government provides public goods and services?**
   - (A) to promote public safety
   - (B) politicians love spending as much of the public's money as they can ✓
   - (C) to keep people healthy
   - (D) to educate citizens

2. **Public goods and services are paid for by _____ .**
   - (F) taxes
   - (G) library fees
   - (H) the entrance fee to a city park
   - (J) all of the above ✓

3. **A type of tax where you pay an amount based on the value of your home is called a(n) _____ .**
   - (A) value-added tax
   - (B) property tax ✓
   - (C) income tax
   - (D) sales tax

4. **A type of tax where you pay an extra amount based on the total price of items you purchase is called a(n) _____ .**
   - (F) value-added tax
   - (G) property tax
   - (H) income tax
   - (J) sales tax ✓

5. **Which of the following is *not* a public service provided by your local government?**
   - (A) snow removal
   - (B) lawn care ✓
   - (C) street repair
   - (D) police protection

6. **Which of the following is an example of government involvement in the economy?**
   - (F) The Union passed an income tax during the Civil War.
   - (G) The federal government created public works projects during the Depression.
   - (H) Industries were converted to war production during World War II.
   - (J) all of the above ✓

DIRECTIONS: For each of the following public goods and services, write an **L** if it is provided by your local (city) government, write an **S** if it is provided by the state government, or write an **N** if it is provided by the U.S. (national) government.

_____ 7. **Post office**

_____ 8. **State patrol**

_____ 9. **Fire department**

_____ 10. **Armed forces**

_____ 11. **City parks**

_____ 12. **Sidewalk repair**

_____ 13. **Driver's license registration**

STOP

SS5E3 # Competition, Markets, and Prices

DIRECTIONS: Choose the best answer.

1. **For years, Phil's Service Station was the only gas station in Smallville. There was no other place to buy gasoline within 30 miles of Phil's. But last week, Biggie Oil Company opened a brand-new gas station about $\frac{1}{4}$ mile from Phil's Service Station. Now that Phil's has a competitor, what do you think will happen to the price of gas at Phil's?**

   (A) It will go down.

   (B) It will go up.

   (C) It will stay the same.

   (D) None of the above. Phil's will be out of business within a few days.

2. **Consumers decide what to buy because of _____ .**

   (F) the quality of a product

   (G) the availability of a product

   (H) the price of a product

   (J) all of the above

3. **Suppose you needed some thing-a-ma-bobs. At what price would you be most likely to purchase the greatest number of them?**

   (A) $1.00

   (B) $2.50

   (C) $5.00

   (D) the same number will be purchased no matter the price

4. **When the price of something goes up, the number of people who want to buy the item usually _____ .**

   (F) goes up also

   (G) goes down

   (H) stays the same

   (J) drops to zero

5. **This fall, Danny decided to charge neighbors $5 per hour to rake leaves. He got a few customers, but not as many as he thought he would. What would most likely happen if Danny lowered his price to $3 per hour?**

   (A) More people would decide to let Danny rake their leaves.

   (B) Danny would make a lot less money.

   (C) Danny would lose most of his customers.

   (D) His friend Alison would start raking leaves too at $5 per hour.

6. **What happens when supply of a product goes down but demand goes up?**

   (F) The price of the product stays the same.

   (G) The price of the product goes down.

   (H) Producers will no longer want to make the product.

   (J) The price of the product goes up.

7. **A big winter storm knocked out power to a community for several days. A local store kept several generators in stock. The generators provided a source of electricity. However, the store did not usually sell very many because they were expensive. When the storm hit the community, the store ran out of generators and had to order more. Why do you think people wanted to purchase the generators even though they were still expensive?**

   _____

   _____

   _____

   _____

Social Studies   **Economics**

SS5E3   Education, Career Choice, and Income

DIRECTIONS: Look at the following types of jobs. If you think the job pays a high salary, place an **H** in the space provided. If you think the job pays a medium salary, place an **M** in the space provided. If you think the job pays a low salary, place an **L** in the space provided.

_____ 1. surgeon

_____ 2. auto mechanic

_____ 3. stockbroker

_____ 4. dishwasher

_____ 5. trash collector

_____ 6. flight engineer

_____ 7. carpenter

_____ 8. cashier

_____ 9. lawyer

DIRECTIONS: Look at the following types of jobs. If you think the job requires a lot of education, place an **E+** in the space provided. If you think the job requires a medium amount of education, place an **E** in the space provided. If you think the job does not require much education at all, place an **E–** in the space provided.

_____ 10. surgeon

_____ 11. auto mechanic

_____ 12. stockbroker

_____ 13. dishwasher

_____ 14. trash collector

_____ 15. flight engineer

_____ 16. carpenter

_____ 17. cashier

_____ 18. lawyer

DIRECTIONS: Compare your answers to questions 1–9 to your answers to questions 10–18. How do you think income and education are related?

19. _____

_____

_____

_____

_____

_____

_____

_____

_____

_____

_____

_____

STOP

Social Studies

Economics

SS5E3

Entrepreneurship

DIRECTIONS: Read the story and then answer the questions.

Ten years ago, Wally Anderson opened his own business: Wally's Computer Repair. Wally's business fixes broken computers and printers. Wally used $25,000 of his own money to buy equipment and rent office space. The bank also loaned him $75,000 to help his business get off the ground. (Of course, Wally had to pay the loan back to the bank.)

When Wally first started his store, he was the only employee. He often worked more than 14 hours every day. But over the years, he has hired others to help him with the work. He hired Marcia Fitzgerald to manage the business's finances. Darius Jackson is the lead repair person. Nine other people also work at Wally's store. Wally is very proud of his employees. He is also proud to own his own business. He hopes one day to own and operate another computer repair shop in another town.

 Clue

An **entrepreneur** is someone who starts, runs, and assumes the risk for a business.

1. **In the above story, who is the entrepreneur?**
   - (A) Darius Jackson
   - (B) Marcia Fitzgerald
   - (C) Wally Anderson
   - (D) all of the employees of Wally's Computer Repair

2. **Entrepreneurs _____ .**
   - (F) always make every decision about a business, no matter how small
   - (G) must sometimes borrow money to get their businesses started
   - (H) never hire people to help with their business
   - (J) can own only one business at a time

3. **Wally took some risks when he began his store 10 years ago. Probably the greatest risk he took was that _____ .**
   - (A) he should not have worked 14-hour days
   - (B) he would have lost a lot of money if his business had failed
   - (C) no one should ever try to operate a business alone
   - (D) he did not know how to fix computers

4. **Which of the following statements is *not* true?**
   - (F) Wally invested a lot of time and money to start his business.
   - (G) Because of Wally, several people have jobs.
   - (H) Ten years ago, Wally did not know for sure if his business would succeed.
   - (J) Now that Wally's business has been around for 10 years, Wally no longer has any risk in running his store.

 STOP

Name _____ Date _____

Social Studies

Personal Budgets

Economics

DIRECTIONS: Read the passage below and then answer the questions on the next page.

Always running out of money? Have no idea where your money goes? Saving for a special trip, activity, or object? If you answered yes to any of these questions, it is time to plan a budget and stick to it. Budgets have a bad rap as being too restrictive or too hard to follow. In reality, a budget can be very simple, and understanding how to use one can help you save for special things. There are three easy steps to follow.

The first step in building a livable budget is to record your spending habits. Look at your expenditures. Do you buy your lunch? Do you buy a soft drink or even water from a machine? You may discover you spend money foolishly. Buying a candy bar for $0.50 every day may seem insignificant, but by the end of the month, it adds up to $15.00. Instead, put a snack in your backpack.

The next step is determining your debits and credits. Look at what money comes in and what goes out. If you have determined your spending habits, you know what your debits are. Credits might be harder to determine if you do not have a job. Determine all the ways you get money. For example, count the dollars you earn or money given to you as presents. How much each week do you have available to spend? What are your sources of income? If you do not have a regular source of income, you need to find ways to make money. Do you have an allowance? Can you negotiate with your parents to raise your allowance? Offer to do more chores or special jobs that will increase your income. Check out the neighborhood. Lawn work and babysitting are two jobs that you might like. Remember, your debits should not be more than your credits.

The last step is determining your cash flow and savings goals. How much money do you have available each week to spend? You might budget a small cash flow for yourself because you want to save for a new pair of skis, which means you might earn $10.00 a week, but only allow yourself to spend $3.00. Look at three important categories. How much money do you wish to save? How much money do you need for essentials? How much money do you want for frivolous activities? Determining the balance between savings goals and cash flow is an important decision for any budget.

GO

1. **Define the following terms. Then write the sentence or phrase that helped you determine the definition.**

   expenditures

   _____

   debit

   _____

   credit

   _____

   cash flow

   _____

2. **List the three steps in preparing a budget.**

   _____

   _____

3. **Describe your current approach to a budget. Use all the vocabulary from question 1 in your response.**

   _____

   _____

   _____

4. **After looking at your current approach to a budget, make yourself a revised budget using the chart below. Be sure that your debits do not exceed your credits!**

Date	Credits	Debits
Total		

STOP

SS5E1–SS5E4

Mini-Test 4

DIRECTIONS: Choose the best answer.

1. **Identify the person who will probably earn the highest income.**

   (A) a high-school dropout who delivers pizza

   (B) a plumber who attended vocational school

   (C) a nuclear engineer with an advanced college degree

   (D) a salesman with an associate's degree in marketing

2. **In a personal budget, _____ .**

   (F) debits should be more than credits

   (G) credits should be more than debits

   (H) cash flow does not affect savings

   (J) you do not need to keep track of spending

3. **In a banking system, interest is _____ .**

   (A) earned by the bank

   (B) earned by depositors

   (C) paid by borrowers

   (D) all of the above

4. **Rudy has enough money to buy one of the following: a DVD, a book, a new shirt, or a new game. He ranks his choices as follows: game, DVD, shirt, book. What is his opportunity cost?**

   (F) the game

   (G) the DVD

   (H) the DVD, shirt, and book

   (J) There is no opportunity cost in this situation.

DIRECTIONS: Read the story and then answer question 5.

   Last holiday season, Ziffle's Department Store had 100 Dancing Danny dolls in stock. Dancing Danny dolls were in high demand last year. Ziffle's was able to charge customers $50 each for the dolls and sold them out in one day. This holiday season, Ziffle's ordered 500 of the dolls. Sadly, the Dancing Danny fad has passed. Very few people want the dolls this year.

5. **Which of the following will Ziffle's most likely charge for Dancing Danny dolls this year?**

   (A) $100

   (B) $75

   (C) $50

   (D) $25

6. **Francine owns and operates Francie's Corner Deli. Because she runs her own business, we would call her a(n) _____ .**

   (F) indirect competitor

   (G) entrepreneur

   (H) socialist

   (J) unemployed person

7. **Not much coffee is grown in the United States. Both Colombia and Brazil grow coffee. One way for the United States to get coffee would be to _____ .**

   (A) buy it from Colombia and Brazil

   (B) trade another product with Brazil for coffee

   (C) trade another product with Colombia for coffee

   (D) all of the above

8. **A type of tax where you pay an extra amount based on what you earn is called a(n) _____ .**

   (F) unemployment tax

   (G) property tax

   (H) income tax

   (J) sales tax

How Am I Doing?

Mini-Test 1 Page 143 **Number Correct**	**9–10** answers correct	**Great Job!** Move on to the section test on page 170.
	5–8 answers correct	**You're almost there!** But you still need a little practice. Review practice pages 128–142 before moving on to the section test on page 170.
	0–4 answers correct	**Oops!** Time to review what you have learned and try again. Review the practice section on pages 128–142. Then retake the test on page 143. Now move on to the section test on page 170.
Mini-Test 2 Page 149 **Number Correct**	**4** answers correct	**Awesome!** Move on to the section test on page 170.
	3 answers correct	**You're almost there!** But you still need a little practice. Review practice pages 145–148 before moving on to the section test on page 170.
	0–2 answers correct	**Oops!** Time to review what you have learned and try again. Review the practice section on pages 145–148. Then retake the test on page 149. Now move on to the section test on page 170.
Mini-Test 3 Page 155 **Number Correct**	**8–9** answers correct	**Great Job!** Move on to the section test on page 170.
	6–7 answers correct	**You're almost there!** But you still need a little practice. Review practice pages 151–154 before moving on to the section test on page 170.
	0–5 answers correct	**Oops!** Time to review what you have learned and try again. Review the practice section on pages 151–154. Then retake the test on page 155. Now move on to the section test on page 170.

How Am I Doing?

Mini-Test 4	8 answers correct	**Awesome!** Move on to the section test on page 170.
Page 167 **Number Correct**	5–7 answers correct	**You're almost there!** But you still need a little practice. Review practice pages 157–166 before moving on to the section test on page 170.
	0–4 answers correct	**Oops!** Time to review what you have learned and try again. Review the practice section on pages 157–166. Then retake the test on page 167. Now move on to the section test on page 170.

Name _____ Date _____

Final Social Studies Test
for pages 128–166

DIRECTIONS: Choose the best answer.

1. **As a citizen, you have a responsibility to take part in your community. All of the following are good ways to do this, *except* _____ .**

   (A) write to the president of a company protesting the treatment of women in the company's commercials

   (B) read the newspaper regularly

   (C) secretly remove books from the library that you think are unpatriotic

   (D) vote in every election

2. **Which of the following actions is unconstitutional?**

   (F) owning a hunting rifle

   (G) reading a book praising the September 11, 2001, attack on the United States

   (H) refusing to serve a customer in a bar because he has had too much to drink

   (J) refusing to serve a customer in a restaurant because she is Asian

3. **The Nineteenth Amendment did what?**

   (A) kept people from voting

   (B) repealed the Eighteenth Amendment

   (C) did away with slavery

   (D) gave women the right to vote

4. **To be accepted as part of the Constitution, a proposed amendment must be ratified by what fraction of the states?**

   (F) one third

   (G) three fourths

   (H) two thirds

   (J) over 50 percent

DIRECTIONS: Read the passage. Then answer the questions.

The most popular snack food in years has hit the stores recently. Everyone wants to try the new Beef-o Chips. These hamburger-flavored potato chips are so popular, the manufacturer is having a hard time keeping up with demand. Grocery stores across the nation have been mobbed by hungry customers looking to buy bags of Beef-os. The local Food Clown store reports that an entire shelf of Beef-os was cleaned out by customers yesterday in about five minutes.

5. **When Beef-os first came out a couple of months ago, each bag cost $1.99. Based on the information in the passage, what do you think Beef-os might be selling for now?**

   (A) 25¢

   (B) 99¢

   (C) $1.99

   (D) $2.99

6. **Explain your answer to question 5.**

   (F) Hamburger-flavored potato chips? Yuck! Who would buy those?

   (G) When supply is high and demand is low, prices usually go down.

   (H) The price was $1.99 just a couple of months ago. That's too soon for any price change to occur.

   (J) When supply is low and demand is high, prices usually rise.

DIRECTIONS: Choose the best answer.

7. **Which of the following towns did not experience growth because of ranching and the westward expansion of the United States in the 19th century?**

   (A) Abilene, Kansas

   (B) San Antonio, Texas

   (C) Boston, Massachusetts

   (D) Cheyenne, Wyoming

GO

8. **This great plant scientist developed many useful techniques in agriculture. He was especially known for his work with peanuts.**

   F Alexander Graham Bell

   ✓ G George Washington Carver

   H Eli Whitney

   J Thomas Edison

DIRECTIONS: Read the passage. Then answer the questions.

In 1850, Congress passed five bills known as the Compromise of 1850. The laws were called a compromise because both Northern and Southern states gave up some things they wanted. For example, the Compromise of 1850 allowed California to be admitted to the United States as a free state. Texas, New Mexico, and Utah could each decide whether they wanted to have slavery. Another part of the Compromise was called the Fugitive Slave Act. This allowed African Americans in the North to be taken back to the South to slavery. It also tried to make people stop helping slaves escape.

9. **The Compromise of 1850 occurred _____ .**

   A just before the start of the American Revolution

   B just after the end of the American Revolution

   C a few years before the Civil War broke out

   D a few years after the Civil War ended

10. **Why do you think Congress passed the Compromise of 1850?**

   F Congress was trying to encourage settlers to move west.

   G Congress was desperately trying to keep the United States together.

   H Congress wanted to encourage hostility between Northern and Southern states.

   J Congress was trying to make it easier for African Americans to find jobs.

DIRECTIONS: Read the passage and study the chart. Use them to answer questions 11–12.

As the Industrial Revolution spread throughout the United States, more and more people from other countries immigrated, or moved, to the United States. In the mid-1800s, many of the immigrants settled in the West and became farmers. But by the late 1800s, most new immigrants were settling in cities and seeking work in factories and mines.

This pictograph shows how many people immigrated to the United States from 1820 to 1920. Each 🧍 stands for 1,000,000 immigrants.

Number of People Who Immigrated to the U.S.
1820–1840
1841–1860
1861–1880
1881–1900
1901–1920

11. **During which years did the greatest number of people immigrate?**

   A 1841–1860

   B 1861–1880

   C 1881–1900

   D 1901–1920

12. **Why did most new immigrants of the late 1800s and early 1900s choose to live in urban areas instead of rural areas?**

   F They did not want to be farmers.

   G They had lived in cities before.

   H They enjoyed city life.

   J They found work in cities.

GO ➡

DIRECTIONS: Study the map below, and then answer the questions that follow.

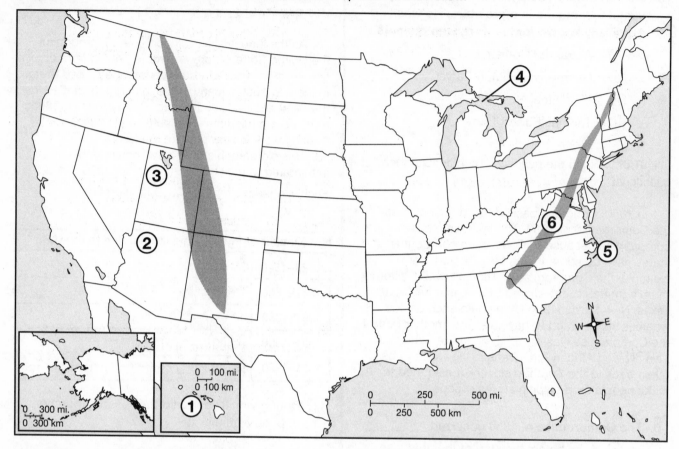

13. **What is the place labeled 1 on the map?**
    - Ⓐ New York City, New York
    - Ⓑ Fort Sumter, South Carolina
    - Ⓒ Pearl Harbor, Hawaii
    - Ⓓ Chicago, Illinois

14. **What is the place labeled 3 on the map?**
    - Ⓕ Great Lakes
    - Ⓖ Great Salt Lake
    - Ⓗ Salton Sea
    - Ⓙ Grand Canyon

15. **What is the place labeled 4 on the map?**
    - Ⓐ Great Lakes
    - Ⓑ Great Salt Lake
    - Ⓒ Salton Sea
    - Ⓓ Grand Canyon

16. **What is the place labeled 5 on the map?**
    - Ⓕ Pittsburgh, Pennsylvania
    - Ⓖ Gettysburg, Pennsylvania
    - Ⓗ Montgomery, Alabama
    - Ⓙ Kitty Hawk, North Carolina

17. **What is the place labeled 6 on the map?**
    - Ⓐ Mojave Desert
    - Ⓑ Rocky Mountains
    - Ⓒ Mississippi River
    - Ⓓ Adirondack Mountains

18. **What is the place labeled 2 on the map?**
    - Ⓕ Mojave Desert
    - Ⓖ Salton Sea
    - Ⓗ Grand Canyon
    - Ⓙ Rocky Mountains

GO

Georgia Test Practice

Name _____ Date _____

DIRECTIONS: Choose the best answer.

19. **Slavery was outlawed in the United States by the _____ .**

    (A) start of the Civil War

    (B) Emancipation Proclamation

    (C) Thirteenth Amendment

    (D) Gettysburg Address

20. **The 1920s are often referred to as the _____ .**

    (F) Great Depression

    (G) Jazz Age

    (H) Age of Reform

    (J) Cold War era

21. **The bombing of Pearl Harbor caused the United States to enter what war?**

    (A) Spanish-American War

    (B) World War I

    (C) World War II

    (D) Vietnam War

22. **The Berlin Wall was built during _____ .**

    (F) the Cold War

    (G) World War I

    (H) World War II

    (J) the Korean War

23. **Which of the following people was a leader of the civil rights movement?**

    (A) Thomas Edison

    (B) Margaret Mitchell

    (C) Martin Luther King, Jr.

    (D) Joseph McCarthy

24. **September 11, 2001, is remembered as the day that _____ .**

    (F) the Allies landed on the coast of Normandy during World War II

    (G) Pearl Harbor was bombed

    (H) Iraq invaded Kuwait

    (J) airliners crashed into the World Trade Center and the Pentagon

25. **The next best alternative that is given up when a choice is made is called _____ .**

    (A) voluntary exchange

    (B) the opportunity cost

    (C) competition

    (D) productivity

26. **Someone who starts, runs, and assumes the risks for a business is called _____ .**

    (F) an entrepreneur

    (G) a banker

    (H) an investor

    (J) a competitor

27. **You need a personal budget if _____ .**

    (A) you are always running out of money

    (B) you have no idea where your money goes

    (C) you need to save money

    (D) all of the above

GO

DIRECTIONS: Study the chart below and then answer the question that follows.

Year	Percent of People Unemployed
1926	1.6
1928	4.2
1930	8.9
1932	24.1
1934	22.0
1936	17.0
1938	19.1
1940	14.6
1942	4.7
1944	1.2
1946	3.9

SOURCE: United States Census Bureau.

28. **The Great Depression, during which millions of people lost their jobs, took place in the _____ .**

    (F)   1920s

    ✓(G)   1930s

    (H)   1940s

    (J)   1950s

STOP

Final Social Studies Test
Answer Sheet

1 Ⓐ Ⓑ Ⓒ Ⓓ
2 Ⓕ Ⓖ Ⓗ Ⓙ
3 Ⓐ Ⓑ Ⓒ Ⓓ
4 Ⓕ Ⓖ Ⓗ Ⓙ
5 Ⓐ Ⓑ Ⓒ Ⓓ
6 Ⓕ Ⓖ Ⓗ Ⓙ
7 Ⓐ Ⓑ Ⓒ Ⓓ
8 Ⓕ Ⓖ Ⓗ Ⓙ
9 Ⓐ Ⓑ Ⓒ Ⓓ
10 Ⓕ Ⓖ Ⓗ Ⓙ

11 Ⓐ Ⓑ Ⓒ Ⓓ
12 Ⓕ Ⓖ Ⓗ Ⓙ
13 Ⓐ Ⓑ Ⓒ Ⓓ
14 Ⓕ Ⓖ Ⓗ Ⓙ
15 Ⓐ Ⓑ Ⓒ Ⓓ
16 Ⓕ Ⓖ Ⓗ Ⓙ
17 Ⓐ Ⓑ Ⓒ Ⓓ
18 Ⓕ Ⓖ Ⓗ Ⓙ
19 Ⓐ Ⓑ Ⓒ Ⓓ
20 Ⓕ Ⓖ Ⓗ Ⓙ

21 Ⓐ Ⓑ Ⓒ Ⓓ
22 Ⓕ Ⓖ Ⓗ Ⓙ
23 Ⓐ Ⓑ Ⓒ Ⓓ
24 Ⓕ Ⓖ Ⓗ Ⓙ
25 Ⓐ Ⓑ Ⓒ Ⓓ
26 Ⓕ Ⓖ Ⓗ Ⓙ
27 Ⓐ Ⓑ Ⓒ Ⓓ
28 Ⓕ Ⓖ Ⓗ Ⓙ

Georgia Science
Content Standards

The science section measures knowledge in five different areas:

Characteristics of Science

    1) **Habits of Mind**

    2) **The Nature of Science**

Content

    3) **Earth Science**

    4) **Physical Science**

    5) **Life Science**

Georgia Science
Table of Contents

Habits of Mind Standards

S5CS1. Students will be aware of the importance of curiosity, honesty, openness, and skepticism in science and will exhibit these traits in their own efforts to understand how the world works. *(See page 179.)*

a. Keep records of investigations and observations and do not alter the records later.
b. Carefully distinguish observations from ideas and speculation about those observations.
c. Offer reasons for findings and consider reasons suggested by others.
d. Take responsibility for understanding the importance of being safety conscious.

S5CS2. Students will have the computation and estimation skills necessary for analyzing data and following scientific explanations. *(See page 180.)*

a. Add, subtract, multiply, and divide whole numbers using mental math, paper/pencil, and a calculator.
b. Use fractions and decimals, and translate between decimals and commonly encountered fractions—halves, thirds, fourths, fifths, tenths, and hundredths (but not sixths, sevenths, and so on)—in scientific calculations.
c. Judge whether measurements and computations of quantities, such as length, area, volume, weight, or time, are reasonable answers to scientific problems by comparing them to typical values.

S5CS3. Students will use tools and instruments for observing, measuring, and manipulating objects in scientific activities. *(See page 181.)*

a. Choose appropriate common materials for making simple mechanical constructions and repairing things.
b. Measure and mix dry and liquid materials in prescribed amounts, exercising reasonable safety.
c. Use computers, cameras, and recording devices for capturing information.
d. Identify and practice accepted safety procedures in manipulating science materials and equipment.

S5CS4. Students will use ideas of system, model, change, and scale in exploring scientific and technological matters. *(See page 182.)*

a. Observe and describe how parts influence one another in things with many parts.
b. Use geometric figures, number sequences, graphs, diagrams, sketches, number lines, maps, and stories to represent corresponding features of objects, events, and processes in the real world. Identify ways in which the representations do not match their original counterparts.
c. Identify patterns of change in things—such as steady, repetitive, or irregular change—using records, tables, or graphs of measurements where appropriate.
d. Identify the biggest and the smallest possible values of something.

S5CS5. Students will communicate scientific ideas and activities clearly. *(See page 183.)*

a. Write instructions that others can follow in carrying out a scientific procedure.
b. Make sketches to aid in explaining scientific procedures or ideas.
c. Use numerical data in describing and comparing objects and events.
d. Locate scientific information in reference books, back issues of newspapers and magazines, CD-ROMs, and computer databases.

Habits of Mind Standards

S5CS6. Students will question scientific claims and arguments effectively. *(See page 183.)*

a. Support statements with facts found in books, articles, and databases, and identify the sources used.

b. Identify when comparisons might not be fair because some conditions are different.

The Nature of Science Standards

S5CS7. Students will be familiar with the character of scientific knowledge and how it is achieved. *(See pages 184–185.)* **Students will recognize the following concepts.**

a. Similar scientific investigations seldom produce exactly the same results, which may differ due to unexpected differences in whatever is being investigated, unrecognized differences in the methods or circumstances of the investigation, or observational uncertainties.

b. Some scientific knowledge is very old and yet is still applicable today.

S5CS8. Students will understand important features of the process of scientific inquiry. *(See page 186.)* **Students will apply the following to inquiry learning practices.**

a. Scientific investigations may take many different forms, including observing what things are like or what is happening somewhere, collecting specimens for analysis, and doing experiments.

b. Clear and active communication is an essential part of doing science. It enables scientists to inform others about their work, expose their ideas to criticism by other scientists, and stay informed about scientific discoveries around the world.

c. Scientists use technology to increase their power to observe things and to measure and compare things accurately.

d. Science involves many different kinds of work and engages men and women of all ages and backgrounds.

Name _____ Date _____

Science

Making Scientific Observations

Habits of
Mind

DIRECTIONS: Choose the best answer.

1. A testable prediction is _____ .

- (A) a hypothesis
- (B) an experiment
- (C) an exercise
- (D) a variable

2. The process of gathering information through the senses is called _____ .

- (F) inferring
- (G) observation
- (H) conclusion
- (J) analyzing

DIRECTIONS: Read the passages. Then answer the questions.

Adam's Experiment

Adam wants to find out how lemon juice reacts when it is combined with different substances. In three separate paper cups, he puts equal amounts of baking soda, salt, and sugar. Then he puts 3 drops of lemon juice into each cup. After 30 seconds, he observes all three cups.

3. What should Adam do if he wants his lab partner to be able to repeat this experiment?

- (A) Keep accurate records of procedures and results.
- (B) Wait until he finishes all the trials before recording any results.
- (C) Estimate the amounts of materials used.
- (D) none of these

Scott's Experiment

After discovering a moldy loaf of bread in a kitchen cabinet, Scott decided to do an experiment to determine the conditions under which mold grows the

best. He suspected that mold grows best in the dark, so he put his idea to the test.

Scott bought a new loaf of bread and some sandwich bags. In each bag, he put a slice of bread, a damp paper towel, and a bit of soil. He put the bags in places that received different amounts of light, but would remain at room temperature.

In three days, Scott checked the bags. He found the most mold growing on the bread that he had put in a dark place.

4. What was Scott's hypothesis?

- (F) Mold grows best in a sandwich bag.
- (G) Mold will take over the world in the year 2009.
- (H) Mold grows best in the dark.
- (J) Mold grows best at room temperature.

5. Which of the following is Scott's observation?

- (A) He bought a new loaf of bread and some sandwich bags.
- (B) He put a slice of bread, a damp paper towel, and a bit of soil in each bag.
- (C) He put the bags in places that received different amounts of light.
- (D) He found the most mold growing on the bread that he had put in a dark place.

6. Which of the following best explains Scott's findings?

- (F) Light affects the growth of mold.
- (G) Temperature does not affect the growth of mold.
- (H) Mold does not need water to grow.
- (J) The sandwich bags made the mold grow.

Science

S5CS2

Using Computations and Estimation Skills

Habits of Mind

 Clue — Choose the best method to help you perform these computations. Use either mental math, pencil and paper, or a calculator to find your answer.

DIRECTIONS: Choose the correct answer to each problem. Choose "none of these" if the correct answer is not given.

1. 132
    × 4

    Ⓐ 528
    Ⓑ 136
    Ⓒ 478
    Ⓓ none of these

2. $1\frac{1}{2} - \frac{3}{4}$

    Ⓕ $1\frac{1}{4}$
    Ⓖ 0.75
    Ⓗ 1.25
    Ⓙ none of these

3. ■ + 6 = 44

    Ⓐ 38
    Ⓑ 50
    Ⓒ 264
    Ⓓ none of these

4. 3)‾90‾

    Ⓕ 3
    Ⓖ 180
    Ⓗ 30
    Ⓙ none of these

5. 2 × 5 × 9 =

    Ⓐ 16
    Ⓑ 19
    Ⓒ 91
    Ⓓ none of these

DIRECTIONS: The following ingredients make one batch of blueberry muffins. Use them to estimate answers for questions 6–7.

$\frac{3}{4}$ cup flour	3 tsp baking powder
$\frac{1}{2}$ tsp salt	$\frac{1}{4}$ cup margarine
$\frac{1}{2}$ cup sugar	1 egg
$\frac{3}{4}$ cup milk	1 tsp vanilla
1 cup frozen blueberries	

6. **To make half of the recipe, how much sugar does she need?**

    Ⓕ about $\frac{1}{4}$ cup
    Ⓖ about $\frac{1}{8}$ cup
    Ⓗ about $\frac{1}{2}$ cup
    Ⓙ about $\frac{3}{8}$ cup

7. **To make $1\frac{1}{2}$ batches of muffins, how many cups of milk does she need?**

    Ⓐ about $1\frac{1}{2}$ cups
    Ⓑ a little more than 1 cup
    Ⓒ not quite 1 cup
    Ⓓ 1 cup

STOP

Name _____ Date _____

Science

S5CS3

Tools and Safety Procedures in Scientific Activities

DIRECTIONS: Choose the best answer.

1. **Which tool would you use to measure the weight of a specimen?**
   - (A) scale
   - (B) ruler
   - (C) clock
   - (D) calendar

2. **Which tool would you use to measure the capacity of a container?**
   - (F) measuring cup
   - (G) calculator
   - (H) scale
   - (J) ruler

3. **Which tool would you use to measure the length of a hummingbird?**
   - (A) ruler
   - (B) scale
   - (C) thermometer
   - (D) protractor

4. **In science class, students had to determine the hours from dusk to dawn. Which tool would you use to measure the number of hours?**
   - (F) calendar
   - (G) clock
   - (H) scale
   - (J) capacity

5. **Phil likes to keep a weather journal. Which tool would he use to measure temperature?**
   - (A) ruler
   - (B) scale
   - (C) thermometer
   - (D) clock

6. **Which instrument would you use to look more closely at a leaf?**
   - (F) barometer
   - (G) thermometer
   - (H) microscope
   - (J) beaker

7. **Which instrument would you use to measure the speed of a falling object?**
   - (A) a stopwatch
   - (B) a microscope
   - (C) a balance scale
   - (D) a ruler

8. **What tool would you use to measure liquids in a science lab?**
   - (F) graduated cylinder
   - (G) beaker
   - (H) Petri dish
   - (J) scalpel

9. **Which of these is an example of unsafe behavior in a science lab?**
   - (A) wearing eye goggles
   - (B) smelling and tasting unknown chemicals
   - (C) avoiding the use of broken or chipped glassware
   - (D) tying back long hair when working with flames

10. **After you have completed a laboratory activity, you should _____ .**
    - (F) use hand protection when handling any items that have been heated
    - (G) clean up your work area
    - (H) wash your hands with soap and water
    - (J) all of the above

Scientific Models and Patterns of Change

DIRECTIONS: Choose the best answer.

1. **Look at the pictures below. Which is the best representation of the sun, Earth, and the moon, overall?**

(A)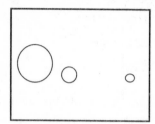

(B)

(C)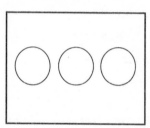

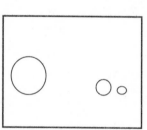

(D)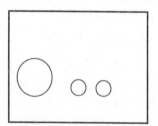

2. **Natalie is trying to explain the solar system to her younger brother. What three objects should she choose to best represent the sun, Earth, and the moon?**

   (F) a chair, a book, and a candle

   (G) paper, a pencil, and a crayon

   (H) a basketball, a softball, and a table tennis ball

   (J) an apple, an orange, and a lemon

3. **By using these three objects to help explain a larger system, Natalie has made a _____ of the solar system.**

   (A) scale

   (B) model

   (C) original

   (D) copy

4. **The planet Venus is often called the "morning star." This is because Venus sometimes rises above the horizon very early in the morning before sunrise. Before sunrise, Venus is often the brightest object in the sky. As the sun rises, Venus becomes fainter and fainter. Predict the day that Venus will rise at 6:00 A.M.**

Day	Time Venus Rises
Sunday	6:24 A.M.
Monday	6:20 A.M.
Tuesday	6:16 A.M.
Wednesday	6:12 A.M.
Thursday	6:08 A.M.

   (F) Thursday

   (G) Friday

   (H) Saturday

   (J) Sunday

Science

Habits of Mind

| S5CS5–S5CS6 |

Locating and Communicating Scientific Data

DIRECTIONS: Use newspapers or other sources to find the average daily temperature in Atlanta for the past week. Fill in the chart below with the data you found. In the space below the chart, construct a bar graph to represent the data. Then answer the questions that follow.

Day	Temperature (°F)
Sunday	
Monday	
Tuesday	
Wednesday	
Thursday	
Friday	
Saturday	

1. **What was the source of your data?**

   _____

   _____

2. **Your grandfather says it's usually hotter in Savannah than in Atlanta in July. How would you verify if this is true?**

   _____

   _____

STOP

Name _____   Date _____

Science

S5CS7

Similar Scientific Investigations

DIRECTIONS: Read the story below and then answer the questions that follow.

> Lauren entered the science fair. For her project, she wanted to see which brand of batteries lasts longest: Everglo, Glomore, or Everlasting. She decided to place new batteries into identical new flashlights, turn on the flashlights, then wait for the batteries to run down. She wrote down the following results: Everglo—lasted 19 hours; Glomore—lasted 17 hours; Everlasting—lasted 25 hours.
>
> She then decided to redo the experiment to confirm the results. For her second experiment, she placed new batteries into the old flashlights that her parents keep in the garage, the kitchen, and their bedroom. She then turned on the flashlights and waited for the batteries to run down. This time she wrote down the following results: Everglo—lasted 13 hours; Glomore—lasted 16 hours; Everlasting—lasted 9 hours.
>
> Lauren was puzzled by the results of her second experiment. Because it was so similar to her first experiment, she thought she would get the same results.

1. **What is the best explanation for why Lauren's second experiment had different results than her first experiment?**

   (A) Lauren used different brands of batteries in the second experiment.

   (B) The second experiment used old flashlights, while the first experiment used new flashlights.

   (C) The second experiment was too much like the first experiment.

   (D) There is no good explanation; sometimes things just happen.

2. **How was Lauren sure that the results of the second experiment were different from the results of the first experiment?**

   (F) She read on the side of the battery packages how long each brand would last before it ran down.

   (G) She simply remembered how long it took each brand of battery to run down.

   (H) She recorded exactly how long it took each brand of battery to run down for each experiment.

   (J) She cannot be sure; her experiment was faulty.

3. **Tell what Lauren did right in her experiments.**

   _____

   _____

   _____

   _____

   _____

   _____

4. **Could she have done anything in a better, more scientific way?**

   _____

   _____

   _____

   _____

S5CS7

Old Scientific Knowledge

DIRECTIONS: Read the passage and then choose the best answers.

Sir Isaac Newton

Sir Isaac Newton, born in 1642, was an English scientist, astronomer, and mathematician. Newton is sometimes described as "one of the greatest names in the history of human thought" because of his great contributions to mathematics, physics, and astronomy.

Newton discovered how the universe is held together through his theory of gravitation. He discovered the secrets of light and color, and he invented a new kind of mathematics, *calculus*. Newton made these three discoveries within 18 months from 1665 to 1667.

1. **Which of Newton's discoveries explains how the universe is held together?**

   (A) calculus

   (B) the theory of light and color

   (C) the theory of gravitation

   (D) the theory of relativity

2. **The new kind of mathematics that Newton invented is called _____ .**

   (F) physics

   (G) astronomy

   (H) gravitation

   (J) calculus

3. **Which of the following statements about Isaac Newton is true?**

   (A) We still use many of Newton's theories and discoveries today.

   (B) Because Newton lived so long ago, most of his theories are no longer valid.

   (C) Newton made important contributions in mathematics, physics, and biology.

   (D) Newton was a brilliant scientist and astronomer, but a poor mathematician.

STOP

Name _____ Date _____

The Process of Scientific Inquiry

DIRECTIONS: Choose the best answer.

1. Jordan lives in a desert and wants to find out if the area has always been a desert. He spends one afternoon gathering rocks and brings them home to study. This is an example of which kind of scientific investigation?

   (A) observation

   (B) experimentation

   (C) collecting specimens for analysis

   (D) none of these

2. Jeannie wanted to find out if warm water was more dense than cold water. She added red food coloring to a beaker of warm water and then used an eyedropper to add the warm, red water to a beaker of cold water. This is an example of what kind of scientific investigation?

   (F) observation

   (G) experimentation

   (H) collecting specimens for analysis

   (J) none of these

3. You are boiling water on your stove next to a window. You notice water droplets on the inside of the window. This is an example of what kind of scientific investigation?

   (A) observation

   (B) experimentation

   (C) collecting specimens for analysis

   (D) none of these

4. Susan wants to learn more about molecules. She reads an article about molecules in the encyclopedia. This is an example of what kind of scientific investigation?

   (F) observation

   (G) experimentation

   (H) collecting specimens for analysis

   (J) none of these

5. Which of the following instruments would be used to study cells?

   (A) telescope

   (B) microscope

   (C) binoculars

   (D) thermometer

6. Which of the following instruments would be used to examine the features of the moon?

   (F) binoculars

   (G) microscope

   (H) thermometer

   (J) telescope

7. It is important for scientists to keep accurate and detailed records so _____ .

   (A) they can decide which scientists they want to work with on future projects

   (B) they can decide who the best scientist is

   (C) more scientists can have jobs

   (D) the results of the experiments can be verified

STOP

Name _____ Date _____

Science

S5CS1–S5CS8

For pages 179–186

Mini-Test 1

DIRECTIONS: Read about Ryan's experiment, and then answer the questions.

Ryan wanted to find out if people could tell the difference between the taste of cold tap water and cold bottled water. He filled one glass pitcher with tap water and another glass pitcher with bottled water. Then he placed the pitchers in the same refrigerator overnight.

1. **Before completing his experiment, Ryan guessed that people would not be able to tell the difference between the two types of water. What part of the scientific process does this guess involve?**

    (A) listing the materials

    (B) stating a hypothesis

    (C) organizing data

    (D) stating a conclusion

2. **What should be the next step in Ryan's experiment?**

    (F) He should ask several people to taste the tap water.

    (G) He should ask several people to taste the bottled water.

    (H) He should ask several people to taste both types of water and guess which one is tap water and which one is bottled water.

    (J) He should ask several people to taste both types of water and tell which one they like the best.

3. **What tool would Ryan use to make sure that all of the people in his experiment are given the same amount of water to drink?**

    (A) measuring cup

    (B) calculator

    (C) scale

    (D) ruler

4. **After Ryan has gathered the data, what should he do with it?**

    _____

    _____

    _____

    _____

    _____

5. **If Ryan repeats his experiment, will he get exactly the same results? Explain your answer.**

    _____

    _____

    _____

    _____

    _____

    _____

DIRECTIONS: Choose the best answer.

6. **Halley's Comet appears at regular intervals. In other words, there is the same amount of time between any two sightings. When would you predict that Halley's Comet will return?**

Sightings of Halley's Comet (Year)
1531
1607
1682
1758
1834
1910
1986

    (F) 2082

    (G) 2062

    (H) 2031

    (J) 2025

Earth Science Standards

S5E1. Students will identify surface features of the earth caused by constructive and destructive processes. *(See pages 189–190.)*

a. Identify surface features caused by constructive processes.
- Deposition (deltas, sand dunes, etc.)
- Earthquakes
- Volcanoes
- Faults

b. Identify and find examples of surface features caused by destructive processes.
- Erosion (water—rivers and oceans, wind)
- Weathering
- Impact of organisms
- Earthquakes
- Volcanoes

c. Relate the role of technology and human intervention in the control of constructive and destructive processes. Examples include the following.
- Seismological studies
- Flood control (dams, levees, storm drain management, etc.)
- Beach reclamation (Georgia coastal islands)

Name _____   Date _____

Science   **Earth Science**

S5E1

Surface Features
of the Earth

DIRECTIONS: Choose the best answer.

1. At the mouth of a river that empties into an ocean, a river delta is formed. The delta is a result of _____ .

   (A) erosion   (C) pollution

   (B) deposition   (D) condensation

2. The Hawaiian Islands were formed as a result of _____ .

   (F) deposition   (H) glaciers

   (G) hurricanes   (J) volcanic activity

3. The Grand Canyon was formed as the result of _____ .

   (A) a volcano   (C) erosion

   (B) an earthquake   (D) a glacier

4. What occurs when weathered rock and organic matter are mixed together?

   (F) soil erosion

   (G) soil formation

   (H) volcanic activity

   (J) flooding

5. During the Ice Age, most of the state of Illinois was covered by a huge glacier that changed the landscape. Which of the following was *not* an effect of the glacier on the landscape of that state?

   (A) New mountains were made.

   (B) The peaks of hills were scraped off.

   (C) Many deep valleys were filled in.

   (D) Soil was transported miles away from its origin.

6. The changes that occurred in the pictures below are probably due to _____ .

   1990

   2000

   (F) pollution

   (G) erosion

   (H) tornadoes

   (J) condensation

7. Christopher was looking at pictures of different mountain ranges in the United States. He was surprised to see that the Appalachian Mountains were smaller and more rounded than the Rocky Mountains. The Appalachian Mountains looked old and worn compared to the Rocky Mountains.

   (A) The effect of wind and water caused erosion, wearing away the mountains.

   (B) Too many people and animals traveled across the mountains, causing them to wear away.

   (C) All of the snowfall was so heavy that it weighted down the mountains and caused them to shrink.

   (D) The water that used to cover Earth wore away parts of the mountains.

GO

8. An earthquake is caused by an abrupt shift in the earth along a fracture, or _____ .

(F) fault

(G) seismic wave

(H) Geiger counter

(J) plate

9. _____ is any process that changes a rock's chemical composition.

(A) Mechanical or physical weathering

(B) Chemical weathering

(C) Oxidation

(D) Erosion

10. _____ is the disintegration of rocks without changing their chemical composition.

(F) Mechanical or physical weathering

(G) Chemical weathering

(H) Oxidation

(J) Deposition

11. Which of the following does *not* cause mechanical weathering?

(A) frost

(B) roots of plants or trees

(C) pollution

(D) abrasion

12. Scientists who study earthquakes in order to predict and prepare for them are called _____ .

(F) meteorologists

(G) seismologists

(H) archaeologists

(J) biologists

13. Which of the following is used for flood control?

(A) dams

(B) levees

(C) windbreaks

(D) both A and B

14. Mt. Rushmore is a huge monument in the state of South Dakota. The faces of four American presidents are carved into the side of a cliff on the mountain. Every few years, workers spend six weeks hanging over the edge of the cliff. They are sealing cracks in the rock with caulk, the same material used to seal around the edges and bottoms of bathtubs. Which kind of weathering are the workers most likely trying to protect Mt. Rushmore from?

(F) weathering caused by chemicals that dissolve the rock

(G) weathering caused by air pollution and acid rain

(H) weathering caused by tourists

(J) weathering caused by freezing of water

15. Look at the picture below. It shows high mountains. The layers are made of sedimentary rock. Before the mountains were formed, the sedimentary rocks were in flat layers. How were the mountains formed?

(A) The rock layers were pushed down.

(B) The rock layers were pulled apart.

(C) The rock layers were pushed up.

(D) The rock layers went in opposite directions.

STOP

Science

S5E1

Earth Science

Mini-Test 2

For pages 189–190

DIRECTIONS: Choose the best answer.

1. What is a mixture of weathered rock and organic matter called?
   - (A) soil
   - (B) limestone
   - (C) carbon dioxide
   - (D) clay

2. Sand dunes are hills of sand that form in deserts and along seashores where winds are strong. Sand dunes are the result of _____ .
   - (F) erosion
   - (G) deposition
   - (H) pollution
   - (J) chemical weathering

3. The islands of Japan were formed by _____ .
   - (A) deposition
   - (B) hurricanes
   - (C) glaciers
   - (D) volcanic activity

4. An abrupt shift in the earth along a fault causes _____ .
   - (F) tornadoes
   - (G) hurricanes
   - (H) earthquakes
   - (J) glaciers

5. Water and wind are the two forces that cause _____ .
   - (A) earthquakes
   - (B) glaciers
   - (C) erosion
   - (D) volcanoes

6. A seismologist studies _____ .
   - (F) weather
   - (G) plants
   - (H) earthquakes
   - (J) fossils

7. Which of the following produces chemical weathering?
   - (A) ice
   - (B) wind
   - (C) roots
   - (D) oxidation

8. Levees are used to _____ .
   - (F) monitor volcanic activity
   - (G) monitor earthquakes
   - (H) control flooding
   - (J) control pollution

9. What term describes a mass of snow and ice in motion?
   - (A) loess deposit
   - (B) glacier
   - (C) outwash
   - (D) abrasion

10. The rock material that was once present on the tops of the Adirondack Mountains is now gone. What happened to this rock material?
    - (F) It was pushed inside the earth.
    - (G) Sharp peaks and ridges formed over the rock material.
    - (H) The rock material became magma.
    - (J) The rock material was eroded.

STOP

Physical Science Standards

S5P1. Students will verify that an object is the sum of its parts.
(See page 193.)

a. Demonstrate that the mass of an object is equal to the sum of its parts by manipulating and measuring different objects made of various parts.

b. Investigate how common items have parts that are too small to be seen without magnification.

S5P2. Students will explain the difference between a physical change and a chemical change. *(See page 194.)*

a. Investigate physical changes by separating mixtures and manipulating (cutting, tearing, folding) paper to demonstrate examples of physical change.

b. Recognize that the changes in the state of water (water vapor/steam, liquid, ice) are due to temperature differences and are examples of physical change.

c. Investigate the properties of a substance before, during, and after a chemical reaction to find evidence of change.

S5P3. Students will investigate electricity, magnetism, and their relationship. *(See page 195.)*

a. Investigate static electricity.

b. Determine the necessary components for completing an electric circuit.

c. Investigate common materials to determine if they are insulators or conductors of electricity.

d. Compare a bar magnet to an electromagnet.

Science   **Physical Science**

S5P1

An Object Is the
Sum of Its Parts

DIRECTIONS: Choose the best answer.

1. A pecan pie weighs 32 ounces. If it is cut into 8 equal pieces, how much will each piece weigh?

   Ⓐ 3 ounces

   Ⓑ 4 ounces

   Ⓒ 5 ounces

   Ⓓ 6 ounces

2. If the same pie is cut into 6 equal pieces, how much will the whole pie weigh?

   Ⓕ 24 ounces

   Ⓖ 30 ounces

   Ⓗ 32 ounces

   Ⓙ 48 ounces

3. An orange has 10 sections. If each section weighs 30 grams, how much does the whole orange weigh?

   Ⓐ 150 grams

   Ⓑ 200 grams

   Ⓒ 300 grams

   Ⓓ 350 grams

4. A box of crayons weighs 80 grams. If the box contains 16 crayons, how much does each crayon weigh?

   Ⓕ 4 grams

   Ⓖ 5 grams

   Ⓗ 6 grams

   Ⓙ 7 grams

5. A loaf of bread weighs 440 grams and is cut into equal-sized slices. If each slice weighs 20 grams, how many slices does the loaf contain?

   Ⓐ 12 slices

   Ⓑ 20 slices

   Ⓒ 22 slices

   Ⓓ 24 slices

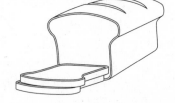

6. A roll of hard candy contains 14 equal pieces. Which of the following statements can be true?

   Ⓕ The roll weighs 28 grams, and each piece weighs 2 grams.

   Ⓖ The roll weighs 28 grams, and each piece weighs 3 grams.

   Ⓗ The roll weighs 42 grams, and each piece weighs 2 grams.

   Ⓙ The roll weighs 30 grams, and each piece weighs 2.5 grams.

7. Which of the following must be magnified to be counted?

   Ⓐ grains of rice

   Ⓑ blades of grass

   Ⓒ leaves on a branch

   Ⓓ fibers in a tissue

8. Which of the following can be seen without magnification?

   Ⓕ the parts of a cell

   Ⓖ crystals of sugar

   Ⓗ the petals of a rose

   Ⓙ grains of pollen

STOP

Name _____ Date _____

Science Physical Science

| S5P2 |

Physical and Chemical Changes

DIRECTIONS: Choose the best answer.

1. **What characteristic best describes what happens during a physical change?**
   - (A) composition changes
   - (B) composition stays the same
   - (C) form stays the same
   - (D) mass is lost

2. **Mixtures are made of substances that are _____ .**
   - (F) chemically changed and can be physically separated
   - (G) chemically changed and cannot be physically separated
   - (H) not chemically changed and can be physically separated
   - (J) not chemically changed and cannot be physically separated

3. **If sugar and sand are mixed, which of the following methods would separate the sugar and sand?**
   - (A) melt the mixture in a pot
   - (B) pour the mixture through a sieve
   - (C) pour the mixture into water to dissolve the sugar
   - (D) They cannot be separated.

4. **How can you change matter from one state to another?**
   - (F) by changing its container
   - (G) by adding or removing heat
   - (H) by dividing it in half
   - (J) by changing its volume

5. **Malcolm left a cube of ice in a glass on a windowsill. In about an hour, the ice changed into a clear substance that took on the shape of the lower part of the glass. Finally, after three days, there appeared to be nothing in the glass at all. What states of matter did the ice cube pass through?**
   - (A) liquid then gas then solid
   - (B) solid then liquid then gas
   - (C) gas then liquid then solid
   - (D) solid then gas then liquid

6. **Jerome wanted to make breakfast. First, he cracked several eggs into a bowl and stirred them briskly. Second, he grated low-fat cheese into the bowl. Third, he ground fresh black pepper into the bowl. After stirring the contents of the bowl, Jerome emptied it into a hot skillet and cooked the ingredients to perfection. Which of the steps is *not* a physical change?**
   - (F) cracking eggs into a bowl
   - (G) grating the cheese
   - (H) grinding the black pepper
   - (J) cooking the eggs

7. **Which of the following sentences describes a chemical change instead of a physical one?**
   - (A) A copper bracelet gets twisted into a new shape.
   - (B) A copper bracelet gets melted into liquid copper.
   - (C) A copper bracelet turns green when it is worn.
   - (D) A copper bracelet is painted red.

STOP

Name _____ Date _____

Science
S5P3

Electricity and Magnetism

DIRECTIONS: Choose the best answer.

1. If Adam rubs a balloon on his hair and holds it up to the wall, what will happen?

   Ⓐ The balloon will be attracted to the wall.

   Ⓑ The wall will repel the balloon.

   Ⓒ The balloon will pop.

   Ⓓ The balloon will float away.

2. Adam's experience with the balloon is an example of _____ .

   Ⓕ static electricity

   Ⓖ conductivity

   Ⓗ insulation

   Ⓙ an electric circuit

3. Rayna puts a magnet into a pile of metal paper clips. What will happen?

   Ⓐ Nothing will happen.

   Ⓑ The paper clips will scatter.

   Ⓒ The paper clips will be attracted to the magnet.

   Ⓓ The magnet will melt the paper clips.

4. What will happen between these two magnets?

N S	N S

   Ⓕ attract

   Ⓖ repel

   Ⓗ not move

   Ⓙ none of these

5. The complete path through which electricity flows is called a _____ .

   Ⓐ sensor

   Ⓑ wire

   Ⓒ circuit

   Ⓓ plug

6. Which of these would *not* make a good insulator?

   Ⓕ an eraser

   Ⓖ a piece of paper

   Ⓗ a paper clip

   Ⓙ a plastic comb

7. Which of these is a conductor of electricity?

   Ⓐ rubber

   Ⓑ water

   Ⓒ plastic

   Ⓓ wood

8. What creates the magnetic field in an electromagnet?

   Ⓕ a bar magnet

   Ⓖ an electric current

   Ⓗ a compass

   Ⓙ an insulator

9. Which of the following is needed to complete the electric circuit in the picture below?

   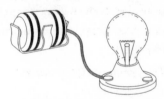

   Ⓐ another lightbulb connected to the battery

   Ⓑ another battery connected to the lightbulb

   Ⓒ another wire connecting the battery to the lightbulb

   Ⓓ nothing is needed

STOP

Science

S5P1–S5P3

For pages 193–195

Mini-Test 3

Physical Science

DIRECTIONS: Study Wally's lab notes and then answer questions 1–2.

Wally's notes
Properties of Mystery Substance X
Freezing Point: 11°C
Boiling Point: 89°C

1. **At which temperature would Mystery Substance X be a liquid?**
   - (A) 4°C
   - (B) 9°C
   - (C) 88°C
   - (D) 92°C

2. **At which temperature would Mystery Substance X be a gas?**
   - (F) 4°C
   - (G) 10°C
   - (H) 88°C
   - (J) 92°C

3. **Magdalena has dropped a box of antique needles in a haystack. Some of the needles are made of wood, some are made of iron, and some are made of bone. If she runs a magnet over the haystack, which needles will she be able to find?**
   - (A) wooden needles
   - (B) iron needles
   - (C) bone needles
   - (D) none of the needles

4. **When water freezes, it changes from a _____ .**
   - (F) gas to a solid
   - (G) liquid to a gas
   - (H) liquid to a solid
   - (J) solid to a gas

5. **What will happen between these two magnets?**

N S	N S

   - (A) attract
   - (B) repel
   - (C) not move
   - (D) not here

6. **Which is an example of a physical change?**
   - (F) metal rusting
   - (G) silver tarnishing
   - (H) water boiling
   - (J) paper burning

7. **Which is an example of a chemical change?**
   - (A) ice cream melting in the sun
   - (B) crushing a soda can
   - (C) mixing salt and sugar
   - (D) burning wood in the fireplace

8. **Which of the following would *not* make a good insulator?**
   - (F) rubber
   - (G) plastic
   - (H) wood
   - (J) metal

9. **A box of chocolate candy has 8 pieces. If the box weighs 45 grams and each piece of candy weighs 20 grams, how much does the whole box of candy weigh?**
   - (A) 80 grams
   - (B) 160 grams
   - (C) 185 grams
   - (D) 205 grams

STOP

Life Science Standards

S5L1. Students will classify organisms into groups and relate how they determined the groups with how and why scientists use classification. *(See page 198.)*

a. Demonstrate how animals are sorted into groups (vertebrate and invertebrate) and how vertebrates are sorted into groups (fish, amphibian, reptile, bird, and mammal).

b. Demonstrate how plants are sorted into groups.

S5L2. Students will recognize that offspring can resemble parents in inherited traits and learned behaviors. *(See page 199.)*

a. Compare and contrast the characteristics of learned behaviors and of inherited traits.

b. Discuss what a gene is and the role genes play in the transfer of traits.

Teacher note: Be sensitive to this topic since biological parents may be unavailable.

S5L3. Students will diagram and label parts of various cells (plant, animal, single-celled, multicelled). *(See pages 200–201.)*

a. Use magnifiers such as microscopes or hand lenses to observe cells and their structure.

b. Identify parts of a plant cell (membrane, wall, cytoplasm, nucleus, chloroplasts) and of an animal cell (membrane, cytoplasm, and nucleus) and determine the function of the parts.

c. Explain how cells in multicelled organisms are similar and different in structure and function to single-celled organisms.

S5L4. Students will relate how microorganisms benefit or harm larger organisms. *(See page 202.)*

a. Identify beneficial microorganisms and explain why they are beneficial.

b. Identify harmful microorganisms and explain why they are harmful.

Science

Life Science

| S5L1 |

Classification of Organisms

DIRECTIONS: Choose the best answer.

1. **Animals that have backbones are called** _____ .

   Ⓐ carnivores
   Ⓑ herbivores
   Ⓒ vertebrates
   Ⓓ invertebrates

2. **Which of the following is an invertebrate?**

   Ⓕ frog   Ⓗ worm
   Ⓖ monkey   Ⓙ bird

3. **Animals that usually have the same body temperature regardless of whether their surroundings are warm or cold are called** _____ .

   Ⓐ cold-blooded
   Ⓑ warm-blooded
   Ⓒ terrestrial
   Ⓓ aquatic

4. **Fish breathe using** _____ .

   Ⓕ lungs   Ⓗ scales
   Ⓖ gills   Ⓙ fins

5. **Which of the following vertebrates is cold-blooded but has lungs?**

   Ⓐ fish   Ⓒ mammals
   Ⓑ birds   Ⓓ reptiles

6. **Animals that spend part of their lives in water and part on land are called** _____ .

   Ⓕ fish   Ⓗ reptiles
   Ⓖ amphibians   Ⓙ mammals

7. **Birds and many insects have** _____ **to help them travel and escape predators.**

   Ⓐ teeth   Ⓒ fins
   Ⓑ stingers   Ⓓ wings

8. **Animals whose babies drink their mother's milk are called** _____ .

   Ⓕ birds   Ⓗ mammals
   Ⓖ fish   Ⓙ reptiles

9. **One difference between a lion cub and a flower seedling is that only the** _____ .

   Ⓐ lion cub needs food
   Ⓑ flower seedling needs water
   Ⓒ lion cub can move from place to place
   Ⓓ flower seedling has parents

10. **How do plants get their food?**

   Ⓕ They get it from outside themselves.
   Ⓖ They create it using photosynthesis.
   Ⓗ They get it during pollination.
   Ⓙ Plants do not need food.

11. **Plants that produce flowers and fruits are** _____ .

   Ⓐ angiosperms
   Ⓑ gymnosperms
   Ⓒ conifers
   Ⓓ lycopsids

12. **Which of the following is an example of a gymnosperm?**

   Ⓕ a tomato plant
   Ⓖ a wildflower
   Ⓗ an apple tree
   Ⓙ a fir tree

STOP

S5L2

Inherited/Learned Traits

DIRECTIONS: For each of the following, put an **I** in the blank if it is an inherited trait. Put an **L** if it is a learned trait.

_____ 1. riding a bike

_____ 2. hair color

_____ 3. the number of petals on a flower

_____ 4. hibernation

_____ 5. counting

_____ 6. eye color

_____ 7. talking

_____ 8. a person's native language

_____ 9. curly or strait tails in pigs

_____ 10. bees stinging

_____ 11. dogs shaking hands

_____ 12. birds laying eggs

13. Inherited traits are transferred from parents to children through _____ , which are the basic units of heredity.

    (A) genes

    (B) microorganisms

    (C) species

    (D) atoms

14. Height is a trait that is inherited, but can be affected by the environment. Give some examples of environmental factors that may affect how tall a person grows to be.

_____

_____

_____

_____

_____

_____

_____

_____

_____

STOP

Name _____   Date _____

Science   Life Science

S5L3   **Plant and Animal Cells**

DIRECTIONS: Read the passage below and then answer the questions that follow.

Cells of Living Things

Cells are the smallest and most basic units of living matter. They are the small pieces that when put together make organs, plants, and even people. All living things are made of cells, though not all cells are exactly alike.

Both animal and plant cells have a cell membrane, which holds all the cell parts together. The nucleus is one of the largest parts of the cell. It is the command center of the cell and controls the activities in the cell. Chromosomes inside this command center control what an organism will be like. For instance, your chromosomes carry the information that makes you have blue or brown eyes or black or red hair. Cytoplasm is the thick liquid that all the parts of the cell float in. It's mostly water, but also has some important chemicals inside.

Both plant and animal cells have mitochondria, which is where food is burned to give the cell energy. Animal and plant cells also have some differences. The plant cell has a cell wall, just outside the cell membrane, that makes the cell stiff. Both animal and plant cells have vacuoles, but animals have far more and they are much smaller. Finally, plant cells have chloroplasts. This is where the cell produces chlorophyll. This chemical makes food for the plant when the sunlight hits it. This is how a plant feeds itself.

Plants and animals are multicelled organisms. Cells that make up multicelled organisms are specialized. Unlike single-celled organisms, such as bacteria, specialized cells found in larger organisms cannot survive outside of the organism. Single-celled organisms carry out all life activities. But specialized cells work as a team to meet the life activities of every cell inside a multicelled organism.

1. **Which part of a cell is the command center?**

   (A)   membrane

   (B)   nucleus

   (C)   cytoplasm

   (D)   mitochondria

2. **In what part of the cell is food burned to give the cell energy?**

   (F)   membrane

   (G)   nucleus

   (H)   cytoplasm

   (J)   mitochondria

3. **What two parts does a plant cell have that an animal cell does not have?**

   (A)   cell wall and chloroplasts

   (B)   membrane and cytoplasm

   (C)   nucleus and cytoplasm

   (D)   nucleus and mitochondria

4. **Which of the following is true of single-celled organisms?**

   (F)   Their cells are specialized.

   (G)   Their cells carry out all life activities.

   (H)   They cannot survive alone.

   (J)   They work as a team with other cells.

Georgia Test Practice

Name _____ Date _____

DIRECTIONS: Use the passage on the previous page to help you fill in the labels of the missing cell part names.

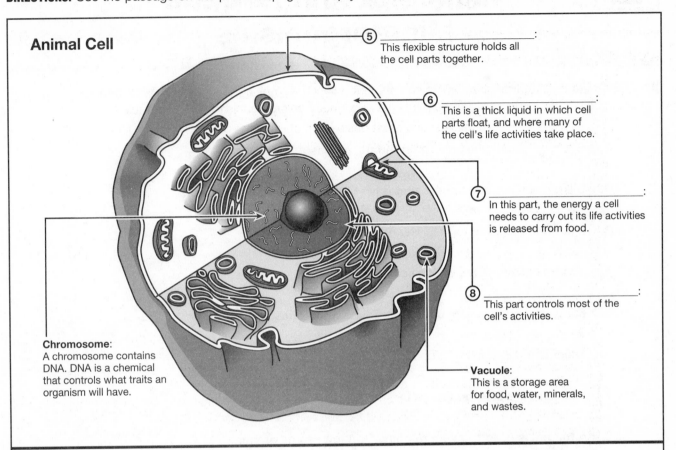

Animal Cell

⑤ _____:
This flexible structure holds all the cell parts together.

⑥ _____:
This is a thick liquid in which cell parts float, and where many of the cell's life activities take place.

⑦ _____:
In this part, the energy a cell needs to carry out its life activities is released from food.

⑧ _____:
This part controls most of the cell's activities.

Chromosome:
A chromosome contains DNA. DNA is a chemical that controls what traits an organism will have.

Vacuole:
This is a storage area for food, water, minerals, and wastes.

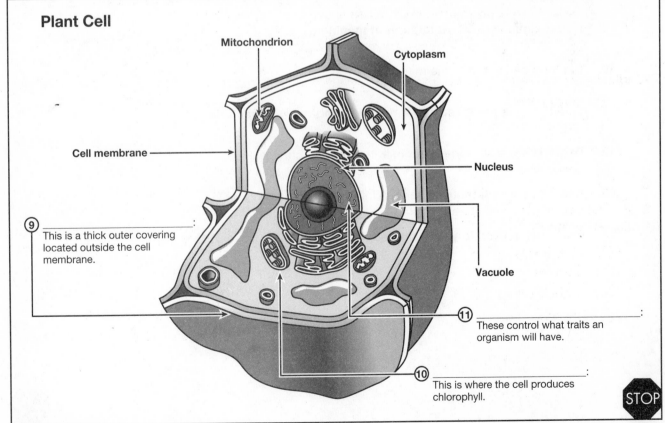

Plant Cell

Mitochondrion

Cytoplasm

Cell membrane

Nucleus

Vacuole

⑨ _____:
This is a thick outer covering located outside the cell membrane.

⑪ _____:
These control what traits an organism will have.

⑩ _____:
This is where the cell produces chlorophyll.

STOP

Science

Life Science

S5L4

Beneficial and Harmful Microorganisms

DIRECTIONS: For each of the following statements, put a **B** in the blank if the statement describes a microorganism that is beneficial or put an **H** if it describes a microorganism that is harmful.

_____ 1. Bacteria cause cholera, an often fatal disease.

_____ 2. Dill pickles are cucumbers that have been fermented by bacteria.

_____ 3. Microbes are used to help clean up oil spills.

_____ 4. A virus causes polio, which sometimes leads to paralysis.

_____ 5. Fungi and bacteria are used to produce antibiotics.

_____ 6. Yeast is used to make bread.

_____ 7. Microbes cause food to spoil.

_____ 8. A fungus is used to make riboflavin, an important vitamin.

_____ 9. A protozoan causes a fatal form of meningitis.

_____ 10. Bacteria cause food poisoning.

_____ 11. Sauerkraut is produced by fermenting cabbage with bacteria.

_____ 12. Bacteria are used to ferment milk to produce cheese.

_____ 13. Bacteria cause tetanus, a serious infectious disease.

_____ 14. One virus is used to vaccinate people against other viruses.

STOP

Georgia Test Practice

Science

Life Science

| S5L1–S5L4 |

For pages 198–202

Mini-Test 4

DIRECTIONS: Choose the best answer.

1. **Which of the following is an example of a vertebrate animal?**
   - (A) fly
   - (B) worm
   - (C) bird
   - (D) starfish

2. **Which of the following traits is inherited?**
   - (F) riding a bike
   - (G) hair color
   - (H) counting
   - (J) talking

3. **Animal cells have _____ .**
   - (A) cell walls
   - (B) chloroplasts
   - (C) cytoplasm
   - (D) large vacuoles

4. **Bacteria are _____ .**
   - (F) always harmful
   - (G) always beneficial
   - (H) neither harmful nor beneficial
   - (J) both harmful and beneficial

5. **A pear tree is an example of _____ .**
   - (A) an angiosperm
   - (B) a gymnosperm
   - (C) a fern
   - (D) a lycopsid

6. **Which part of plant and animal cells contains chromosomes?**
   - (F) nucleus
   - (G) cytoplasm
   - (H) membrane
   - (J) vacuole

7. **Most fish have _____ to protect their bodies.**
   - (A) hair
   - (B) scales
   - (C) feathers
   - (D) skin

8. **Which of the following is a learned trait?**
   - (F) skin color
   - (G) reading
   - (H) straight or curly hair
   - (J) tadpoles turning into frogs

9. **Which of the following statements is true of reptiles?**
   - (A) They are cold-blooded.
   - (B) They have gills.
   - (C) Their babies drink their mother's milk.
   - (D) They spend part of their lives in the water and part of their lives on land.

10. **Which of the following is an example of a harmful microorganism?**
    - (F) Mold is used to produce penicillin.
    - (G) Bacteria are used to produce yogurt.
    - (H) Yeast is used to ferment grapes.
    - (J) A virus causes AIDS.

11. **Which class of vertebrate is warm-blooded, hatches, and breathes using lungs?**
    - (A) mammals
    - (B) birds
    - (C) fish
    - (D) reptiles

STOP

How Am I Doing?

Mini-Test 1 Page 187 **Number Correct** [ ]	**6** answers correct	**Great Job!** Move on to the section test on page 206.
	5 answers correct	**You're almost there!** But you still need a little practice. Review practice pages 179–186 before moving on to the section test on page 206.
	0–4 answers correct	**Oops!** Time to review what you have learned and try again. Review the practice section on pages 179–186. Then retake the test on page 187. Now move on to the section test on page 206.
Mini-Test 2 Page 191 **Number Correct** [ ]	**9–10** answers correct	**Awesome!** Move on to the section test on page 206.
	5–8 answers correct	**You're almost there!** But you still need a little practice. Review practice pages 189–190 before moving on to the section test on page 206.
	0–4 answers correct	**Oops!** Time to review what you have learned and try again. Review the practice section on pages 189–190. Then retake the test on page 191. Now move on to the section test on page 206.
Mini-Test 3 Page 196 **Number Correct** [ ]	**8–9** answers correct	**Great Job!** Move on to the section test on page 206.
	5–7 answers correct	**You're almost there!** But you still need a little practice. Review practice pages 193–195 before moving on to the section test on page 206.
	0–4 answers correct	**Oops!** Time to review what you have learned and try again. Review the practice section on pages 193–195. Then retake the test on page 196. Now move on to the section test on page 206.

How Am I Doing?

Mini-Test 4	9–11 answers correct	**Awesome!** Move on to the section test on page 206.
Page 203 **Number Correct**	5–8 answers correct	**You're almost there!** But you still need a little practice. Review practice pages 198–202 before moving on to the section test on page 206.
	0–4 answers correct	**Oops!** Time to review what you have learned and try again. Review the practice section on pages 198–202. Then retake the test on page 203. Now move on to the section test on page 206.

Name _____   Date _____

Final Science Test
for pages 179–202

DIRECTIONS: Use the information from the graph to answer the questions.

Anthony did an experiment to see how the flight of a paper airplane would be affected by changing the angle of the airplane's wings. He constructed three paper airplanes, slanting the wings down on Plane 1, and slanting them up on Plane 2. The wings of Plane 3 were level.

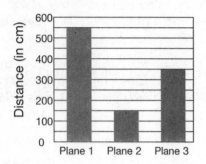

1. **Which of the following statements is *not* true?**

    (A) Plane 1 flew more than twice as far as Plane 2.

    (B) Plane 3 flew half as far as Plane 1.

    (C) Plane 2 flew 400 centimeters less than Plane 1.

    (D) Plane 2 flew less than half as far as Plane 3.

2. **Anthony might have decided to make a graph because it made it easier to _____ .**

    (F) keep his data organized

    (G) compare the distances each plane flew

    (H) draw conclusions about his data

    (J) all of the above

3. **Which of the following conclusions can Anthony draw from the graph?**

    (A) Paper airplanes fly best with their wings pointed up.

    (B) Paper airplanes fly best with level wings.

    (C) Paper airplanes fly best with their wings pointed down.

    (D) Real airplanes fly best with level wings.

DIRECTIONS: Choose the best answer.

4. **Fatima went to the library. She looked up the average amount of rain that fell in Jacksonville, Florida, during the month of November for each of the last 10 years. What can she predict with this information?**

    (F) She can predict about how much it will rain in Jacksonville, Florida, next April.

    (G) She can predict about how much it will rain in Chicago, Illinois, next November.

    (H) She can predict about how much it will rain in Jacksonville, Florida, next November.

    (J) She can predict about how much it will rain in Fort Myers, Florida, next November.

5. **What results in a change in a rock's composition?**

    (A) chemical weathering

    (B) ice wedging

    (C) leaching

    (D) mechanical weathering

6. **What is it called when rocks break down without changing in chemical composition?**

    (F) chemical weathering

    (G) oxidation

    (H) mechanical weathering

    (J) leaching

Georgia Test Practice

7. Study the chart below. What will the moon phase probably be on March 27?

Date	Moon Phase
December 29	Full moon
January 5	Last quarter
January 11	New moon
January 19	First quarter
January 27	Full moon
February 3	Last quarter
February 10	New moon
February 18	First quarter
February 26	Full moon

(A) full moon

(B) last quarter

(C) new moon

(D) first quarter

8. Renaldo shuffles his feet as he walks across the carpet on a cool, dry day. What will happen when he touches the TV screen?

(F) The TV will turn on.

(G) The TV will turn off.

(H) A spark will pass between Renaldo and the TV.

(J) Nothing will happen.

9. When water melts from an ice cube, this is an example of a physical change. The water changes from a _____ .

(A) solid to a gas

(B) liquid to a vapor

(C) solid to a liquid

(D) liquid to solid

10. Tuesday afternoon there was a summer shower in Dallas. The next day, Josh noticed the water puddle on the sidewalk in front of his house was becoming smaller and smaller. Which of the following explains what happened to the water?

(F) It was absorbed by the sidewalk.

(G) It turned into a gas.

(H) It melted.

(J) It froze.

11. Study the table below. Predict which season the southern hemisphere will have during the month of September.

Month	Northern Hemisphere	Southern Hemisphere
December	Winter	Summer
March	Spring	Autumn
June	Summer	Winter
September	Autumn	?

(A) autumn

(B) winter

(C) summer

(D) spring

12. When water enters a crack in a rock and then freezes, what will possibly happen to the rock?

(F) The crack might get larger and split the rock.

(G) The rock might become stronger due to the ice.

(H) The rock might melt and change into an igneous rock.

(J) none of these

GO

Name _____ Date _____

DIRECTIONS: Read the passage and use it to answer questions 13–14.

Earth is a restless place. Although it may seem perfectly solid to you, the earth below your feet is moving at this very moment! The continents rest on top of the brittle crust of the earth, which has broken apart into pieces. These pieces are called *tectonic plates.* They float around on top of the molten interior of the earth, much like crackers floating in a bowl of soup. Molten rock, or lava, continues to push up through cracks in the plates. This pushes the plates even farther apart. The continents used to be closer together. Over the years, they have drifted farther apart, at the rate of about one inch every year.

13. **According to this passage, why do tectonic plates move around?**

Ⓐ They are floating on water.

Ⓑ Molten rock pushes up through the crack and pushes them apart.

Ⓒ The continents are drifting apart.

Ⓓ The crust of the earth is breaking.

14. **According to this passage, how long would it take for Europe and North America to move one foot farther apart?**

Ⓕ 6 years

Ⓖ 8 years

Ⓗ 10 years

Ⓙ 12 years

15. **Which of the following is an inherited trait?**

Ⓐ eye color

Ⓑ hair color

Ⓒ skin color

Ⓓ all of the above

16. **Which of the following is a learned characteristic?**

Ⓕ shoe size

Ⓖ height

Ⓗ the ability to read

Ⓙ all of the above

17. **Study the table below. Which month is likely to have the most hurricanes?**

Table of Tropical Storms and Hurricanes (1886–1996)		
Month Formed	Tropical Storms	Hurricanes
January–April	4	1
May	14	3
June	57	23
July	68	35
August	221	?
September	311	?
October	188	?
November	42	22
December	6	3

Ⓐ July

Ⓑ August

Ⓒ September

Ⓓ October

18. **If you use balls to explain the structure of a molecule, you have made _____ .**

Ⓕ a scale

Ⓖ a model

Ⓗ an original

Ⓙ a copy

19. **Deltas and sand dunes are examples of _____ .**

Ⓐ erosion

Ⓑ deposition

Ⓒ volcanic activity

Ⓓ seismic activity

20. **Which is an example of a chemical change?**

Ⓕ water boiling

Ⓖ metal rusting

Ⓗ ice melting

Ⓙ a rock being crushed

GO

Georgia Test Practice

21. **Which of the following could you use to conduct electricity?**

- (A) metal wire
- (B) tree branch
- (C) plastic drinking straw
- (D) rubber tube

22. **Why would a nail be attracted to a magnet?**

- (F) It is made of steel or iron.
- (G) It weighs less than the magnet.
- (H) It is thinner than the magnet.
- (J) all of the above

23. **In an electromagnet, the electric current passing through the coil of wire creates _____ .**

- (A) static electricity
- (B) a magnetic field
- (C) a chemical change
- (D) a physical change

24. **Johann showed a rock to his Aunt Gordy, a geologist. She said that it looked as though it had been in a river or stream for a long time. Which of the following is most likely true?**

- (F) The rock contains stripes of lots of colors.
- (G) The rock contains very old fossils.
- (H) The rock is rough with very sharp edges.
- (J) The rock is smooth with rounded edges.

25. **What instrument would you use to study microorganisms?**

- (A) barometer
- (B) thermometer
- (C) telescope
- (D) microscope

26. **Chromosomes are found in the _____ of a cell.**

- (F) membrane
- (G) cytoplasm
- (H) nucleus
- (J) mitochondria

27. **Which of the following is an example of a beneficial microorganism?**

- (A) a fungus causing an infection
- (B) bacteria causing whooping cough
- (C) microbes controlling insect pests
- (D) a virus causing hepatitis

28. **Which of the following animals are warm-blooded?**

- (F) fish
- (G) mammals
- (H) amphibians
- (J) reptiles

29. **A tomato plant is an example of _____ .**

- (A) an angiosperm
- (B) a gymnosperm
- (C) a fern
- (D) a lycopsid

STOP

Final Science Test

Answer Sheet

1 Ⓐ Ⓑ Ⓒ Ⓓ
2 Ⓕ Ⓖ Ⓗ Ⓙ
3 Ⓐ Ⓑ Ⓒ Ⓓ
4 Ⓕ Ⓖ Ⓗ Ⓙ
5 Ⓐ Ⓑ Ⓒ Ⓓ
6 Ⓕ Ⓖ Ⓗ Ⓙ
7 Ⓐ Ⓑ Ⓒ Ⓓ
8 Ⓕ Ⓖ Ⓗ Ⓙ
9 Ⓐ Ⓑ Ⓒ Ⓓ
10 Ⓕ Ⓖ Ⓗ Ⓙ

11 Ⓐ Ⓑ Ⓒ Ⓓ
12 Ⓕ Ⓖ Ⓗ Ⓙ
13 Ⓐ Ⓑ Ⓒ Ⓓ
14 Ⓕ Ⓖ Ⓗ Ⓙ
15 Ⓐ Ⓑ Ⓒ Ⓓ
16 Ⓕ Ⓖ Ⓗ Ⓙ
17 Ⓐ Ⓑ Ⓒ Ⓓ
18 Ⓕ Ⓖ Ⓗ Ⓙ
19 Ⓐ Ⓑ Ⓒ Ⓓ
20 Ⓕ Ⓖ Ⓗ Ⓙ

21 Ⓐ Ⓑ Ⓒ Ⓓ
22 Ⓕ Ⓖ Ⓗ Ⓙ
23 Ⓐ Ⓑ Ⓒ Ⓓ
24 Ⓕ Ⓖ Ⓗ Ⓙ
25 Ⓐ Ⓑ Ⓒ Ⓓ
26 Ⓕ Ⓖ Ⓗ Ⓙ
27 Ⓐ Ⓑ Ⓒ Ⓓ
28 Ⓕ Ⓖ Ⓗ Ⓙ
29 Ⓐ Ⓑ Ⓒ Ⓓ

Answer Key

Pages 8–9

1. a little boy's house, which is on a small lake; most of the story takes place in his bedroom
2. Steven; at the time of the action of the story, Steven is eight
3. C
4. Steven believes the stories that his older brother tells him. He adds interesting facts about the lake and creates a childhood fear that makes him overreact when his mom calls for help.
5. Steven tells the story as an adult or older person (his age is not stated). He enjoys the silliness of his childhood fear. He says, "I was just a little kid. I didn't know any better."
6. No. He states, "It didn't seem so scary any more."
7. Answers will vary. The story has humorous qualities that suggest its purpose is to entertain and poke fun at childhood fears.

Page 10

1. C
2. F
3. B
4. F
5. C
6. J

Page 11

1. D
2. H
3. A
4. G

Pages 12–13

1. M, S, S, S
2. Sollie is athletic and graceful but sinks in the water and was being thrown around behind the boat when he forgot to let go of the rope.
3. B
4. Answers will vary. One possible answer: like a dolphin racing down the coast.
5. Sollie is a seal, sleek and smooth in the water.

Page 14

1. zooming
2. plink
3. rustling
4. pitter-patter
5. the park
6. Answers will vary. Possible answer: "Wait for me, Brian" and "Sit here and eat, and don't move until I come back to get you."
7. Answers will vary. Possible answer: There were sizzling burgers on the grill, freshly-popped popcorn, and big barrels of fizzing root beer.

Page 15

1. sandpaper
2. the cat and the electric sander
3. no; free-verse poems often break lines in the middle of sentences
4. a sharp bit of twig stuck in her fur
5. Students' poems will vary. They should be written in free verse.

Page 16

1. The rhyme scheme of the poem is a, b, a, b, c, c.
   a—shore, more
   b—see, free
   c—above, love
2. Answers will vary, but all words should rhyme and should relate to the ocean.

Page 17

1. D
2. G
3. Answers will vary. Possible answers: My dog is so ugly, even my cat feels sorry for him. I am so tired, I can't walk another step.

Page 18

1. why the sun and moon appear in the sky
2. why porcupines have four claws on each foot and why there are four winter months
3. One Who Walks All Over the Sky and Walking About Early; Porcupine and Beaver
4. They were competitive and wanted to change their environments.

Pages 19–20

1. Setting: a public market in a British-governed town
2. Main characters: the black-eyed rebel, who was a young girl, and a young boy
3. Plot: A young girl has letters from families to men fighting for freedom. A young boy has letters from the men to their families. An exchange has to take place right in front of the enemy.
4. Episodes: A boy came into the city with a wagonload of apples and potatoes to sell. A girl offered him a kiss for 12 apples.
5. Climax: The black-eyed rebel bravely marched up to the young boy and asked for a dozen apples for a kiss. While she had her arms around his neck, they quickly exchanged their

packages of letters.
6. Resolution: The black-eyed rebel was going to deliver the letters she received.
7. Refrain: "the corner of her eye" and "her eye"

Pages 21–22
1. 1914
2. the United States
3. Isthmus
4. Panama
5. Atlantic
6. Pacific
7. to link the Atlantic and Pacific Oceans
8. disease
9. excavate earth to clear passages
10. build a dam across the Chagres River
11. build the series of locks
12. cost $380 million
13. runs 50 miles across the Isthmus of Panama
14. water in the canal is controlled by three sets of locks
15. The Republic of Panama has responsibility for administration, upkeep, and maintenance of the canal.
16. The United States built the canal from 1907 to 1914 and operated the canal prior to 1999.
17. The 1903 treaty gave the United States permission to build and operate the canal.
18. The 1977 treaty transferred the responsibility for administration, upkeep, and maintenance of the canal to the Republic of Panama.

Page 23
1. B
2. J
3. C
4. J

Page 24
1. C
2. Answers may vary. Two possible answers are: (1) the illustration emphasizes the strange, eerie nature of the statues and (2) the map shows the remoteness of Easter Island, which contributes to its mystery.

Pages 25–26
1. **1783:** first real balloon flight (with animals); first people to fly in a balloon; first flight in a hydrogen balloon; **1784:** Ballooning became popular in France; **1863:** A balloon corps flew for the Union Army.
2. C
3. J
4. A
5. T
6. F
7. F
8. T
9. T
10. F

Pages 27–28
1. Color signals of red, blue, and green are added to the video signals.
2. The camera changes the light waves into electronic signals; video is produced.
3. The first television system was made.
4. Philo Farnsworth experiments with an idea to send pictures and sound through the air.
5. Television is invented.
6. Television has become one of the world's most important forms of communication, allowing people instant access to current events.
7. Electronic signals from the scene being televised are passed through the air.
8. The stage is set for the invention of television.
9. Electric signals are unscrambled and changed into the original light and sound waves.
10. Televisions have wider screens and clearer pictures.

Pages 29–30
1. D
2. J
3. B
4. H
5. C
6. G
7. B

Page 31
1. ancient Rome
2. F
3. F
4. C

Pages 32–33
Mini-Test 1
1. B
2. H
3. A
4. G
5. C
6. F
7. C
8. J
9. C
10. Cause: Pocahontas knelt beside the Englishman and placed her head on his; Effect: During her year of captivity, she met and married John Rolfe, a Virginia tobacco planter.
11. G
12. Answers will vary, but students should give reasons for their choices.

Page 36
1. C
2. F
3. C
4. H

Page 37
1. B
2. G
3. C
4. F
5. B
6. H
7. B
8. G
9. A

Page 38

1. C
2. F
3. A
4. J
5. C
6. F
7. B
8. H
9. again
10. not
11. can be
12. a person who
13. being
14. after

Page 39

1. B
2. G
3. A
4. J
5. A
6. J

Page 40

1. D
2. F
3. H
4. A
5. G
6. B
7. C
8. E

Page 41

1. D
2. G
3. D
4. F
5. C
6. J
7. D

Page 42

1. week
2. sale
3. meet
4. blew
5. Answers may vary. Possible answers: beautiful, attractive, cute.
6. Answers may vary. Possible answers: burning, scorching, boiling.

7. Answers may vary. Possible answers: ugly, homely, unattractive.
8. Answers may vary. Possible answers: cold, chilly, freezing.
9. C
10. G
11. A
12. H
13. B
14. J

Page 43

1. D
2. G
3. C
4. F
5. C
6. G
7. D
8. J

Page 44
Mini-Test 2

1. B
2. F
3. A
4. H
5. B
6. G
7. A
8. F
9. D
10. H

Page 48

Answers will vary, but students' paragraphs should explain an activity using a logical order of directions and sufficient detail.

Pages 49–50

1–6. Students should decide the plots, the settings, the characters, and the points of view of the stories. They should describe the personalities of their characters.

Students should write short stories that have adequately developed plots and settings. The points of view should be appropriate to the types of stories. The stories should include sensory details used in a way that develops the plot and characters. Students should use at least one narrative device, such as dialogue, suspense, or figurative language to help enhance their plots. The stories should have clear beginnings, middles, and ends.

Pages 51–52

1. Students should indicate what they believe are the effects of violence in the media.
2. Students should indicate any graphs, charts, or other statistical materials that support the topic of the composition.
3. Students should include sources to support the topic.
4. Students should provide thought-out solutions.
5. Informational compositions should include a clear statement of purpose.

Students should define and defend their opinions with at least two supporting details. Compositions should conclude with a summary statement.

Pages 53–54

1. Answers may vary but should take into account the setting and language used by the characters. A possible answer is in medieval England.
2. Answers may vary. Possible answers: The dialect is old-fashioned, belonging to a different time than today. Characters may be dressed in royal-looking garb.
3. Rowan's pony is "little larger than a dog." She is referred to as a "child."
4. He is described as being "evil" and having a "huge form." When he speaks, the story says "he roared." One of the horsemen trembles in his presence.
5. Answers will vary. The reason is not stated in the passage. Students should explain why they think Rowan was trying to escape. Possible answer: Rowan was a mystic and the

lord did not want mystics in his land. There is a reference to the lord "having little patience for one who lets a mystic escape."

Pages 55–56

1–3. Students should state their position, present evidence that supports their position, and state and refute arguments that oppose their position. Students should write a persuasive composition in response to the prompt, "The world would be a better place without. . . ." Students should state their position clearly and then present at least three reasons why they made their assertions. Their writing should demonstrate that they have considered and addressed points on which others may disagree.

Page 57

1. B
2. H
3. D
4. H
5. A
6. H

Pages 58–59

1. C
2. Possible answers include bendable, limber, movable.

3. Possible answers include rigid, immovable.
4. Possible answers include relaxing on one's back, lying flat.
5. book, encyclopedia article, and magazine article
6. the encyclopedia article
7. volume 12
8. pages 25–32
9. the book
10. H
11. A
12. G
13. D
14. G
15. C

Page 60

1. A
2. G
3. C
4. G
5. Students' sentences should be appropriate closing statements for the paragraph.

Pages 61–62
Mini-Test 3

1. B
2. J
3. D
4. H
5. D
6. J
7–9. Student's paragraphs should give a detailed description of the funniest thing that has happened to him or her, an explanation of his or her favorite sport or game, and a convincing argument about making a class

outing to a local amusement park.

Page 64

N: river, Mara, swimmer, bottles
PRON: you, it
V: said, bother, like, think
ADJ: strong, fast, rusty
ADV: badly
PREP: with
C: or
I: Oh

Page 65

1. Answers will vary. Possible answer: and clouds are floating by.
2. Answers will vary. Possible answer: but I stayed home with my sister.
3. Answers will vary. Possible answer: and we raced to see who was there.
4. D
5. J
6. D
7. F

Page 66

1. IN
You are on a deserted island: no town, no people—just you and those crazy, noisy seagulls.
2. EX
I think Mama forgot me. Otherwise, she would come and find me. Mama said not to go see the toys because I'd get lost.
3. NONE
Maggie bit her lip. There was no use crying about it. She pulled her math homework out of the sink

and just stared at her little sister.
4. IM
What you are about to read is so amazing that you simply *must* hear about it now.
5. compound
6. complex
7. simple
8. simple
9. complex
10. compound

Page 67

1. C
2. I can ride faster than you can. Let's race to the stop sign.
3. I'm thirsty. Does anyone have some bottled water?
4. We need to be careful on the bike trail. In-line skaters can appear fast.
5. C
6. I love the playground. It has great swings.
7. When I swing too high, I get sick. Do you?
8. C
9. This ride was fun. Let's do it again tomorrow.
10–13. Students' answers will vary, but they should correctly rewrite each fragment into a complete sentence.

Page 68

1. B
2. H
3. A
4. J
5. B
6. F
7. led

8. where
9. due
10. it's
11. there
12. here
13. you're
14. read
15. sent

Page 69
Mini-Test 4
1. I
2. PRON
3. V
4. ADJ
5. C
6. ADV
7. PREP
8. N
9. its
10. They're
11. wear
12. B
13. J
14. B
15. F
16. C

Pages 73–77
Final English/ Language Arts Test
1. B
2. G
3. C
4. J
5. A
6. H
7. A
8. H
9. D
10. G
11. C
12. G
13. B
14. G
15. C
16. G
17. C
18. G
19. B
20. F
21. D
22. F
23. B
24. H
25. D
26. H
27. B
28. F
29. C
30. F
31. D
32. G
33. C
34. H
35. B
36. J
37. B

Page 82
1. D
2. F
3. D
4. J
5. C
6. G
7. A
8. J

Page 83
1. C
2. J
3. B
4. F
5. D
6. H

Page 84
1. C
2. G
3. C
4. J
5. D
6. H
7. D
8. G

Page 85
1. C
2. F
3. A
4. G
5. A
6. H
7. D
8. G
9. C
10. G

Page 86
1. C
2. F
3. D
4. F
5. C
6. G

Page 87
1. A
2. J
3. B
4. H
5. D
6. H

Page 88

$\times$	$\frac{3}{5}$	$\frac{1}{2}$	$\frac{2}{3}$	$\frac{1}{6}$	$\frac{8}{8}$
$\frac{1}{2}$	$\frac{3}{10}$	$\frac{1}{4}$	$\frac{1}{3}$	$\frac{1}{12}$	$\frac{1}{2}$
$\frac{3}{8}$	$\frac{9}{40}$	$\frac{3}{16}$	$\frac{1}{4}$	$\frac{1}{16}$	$\frac{3}{8}$
$\frac{4}{7}$	$\frac{12}{35}$	$\frac{2}{7}$	$\frac{8}{21}$	$\frac{2}{21}$	$\frac{4}{7}$
$\frac{5}{8}$	$\frac{3}{8}$	$\frac{5}{16}$	$\frac{5}{12}$	$\frac{5}{48}$	$\frac{5}{8}$
$\frac{1}{10}$	$\frac{3}{50}$	$\frac{1}{20}$	$\frac{1}{15}$	$\frac{1}{60}$	$\frac{1}{10}$

1. $7 \div \frac{1}{3} = \frac{7}{1} \div \frac{1}{3} = \frac{7}{1} \times \frac{3}{1} = \frac{21}{1} = 21$

2. $16 \div \frac{1}{3} = \frac{16}{1} \div \frac{1}{3} = \frac{16}{1} \times \frac{3}{1} = \frac{48}{1} = 48$

3. $6 \div \frac{1}{2} = \frac{6}{1} \div \frac{1}{2} = \frac{6}{1} \times \frac{2}{1} = \frac{12}{1} = 12$

4. $3\frac{1}{9} \div \frac{1}{3} = \frac{28}{9} \div \frac{1}{3} = \frac{28}{9} \times \frac{3}{1} = \frac{84}{9} = 9\frac{1}{3}$

5. $8 \div \frac{1}{2} = \frac{8}{1} \div \frac{1}{2} = \frac{8}{1} \times \frac{2}{1} = \frac{16}{1} = 16$

6. $2\frac{1}{2} \div \frac{1}{2} = \frac{5}{2} \div \frac{1}{2} = \frac{5}{2} \times \frac{2}{1} = \frac{10}{2} = 5$

7. $18 \div \frac{1}{7} = \frac{18}{1} \div \frac{1}{7} = \frac{18}{1} \times \frac{7}{1} = \frac{126}{1} = 126$

8. $5\frac{1}{4} \div \frac{3}{8} = \frac{21}{4} \div \frac{3}{8} = \frac{21}{4} \times \frac{8}{3} = \frac{168}{12} = 14$

Page 89

1. $\dfrac{9}{10}$

2. $\dfrac{19}{20}$

3. $\dfrac{8}{15}$

4. $30\dfrac{13}{21}$

5. $91\dfrac{1}{6}$

6. $179\dfrac{1}{2}$

7. $\dfrac{1}{12}$

8. $\dfrac{4}{15}$

9. $\dfrac{1}{18}$

10. $2\dfrac{1}{2}$

11. $5\dfrac{11}{24}$

12. $5\dfrac{5}{8}$

Page 90

1. $<$
2. $>$
3. $=$
4. $<$
5. $>$
6. $=$
7. $<$
8. $<$
9. $=$
10. $=$
11. $<$
12. $<$
13. $<$
14. $>$
15. $<$
16. $=$
17. $<$
18. $>$
19. $>$
20. $<$

Page 91

1. B
2. J
3. Students' circle graphs should reflect the proper proportions.
4. 30%, 10%

Page 92

Mini-Test 1

1. C
2. J
3. A
4. G
5. B
6. H
7. C
8. G
9. A

Page 94

1. 22 square units
2. 16 square units
3. 14 square units
4. 38 square units
5. 40 square units
6. 50 square units
7. 28 square units
8. 18 square units

Page 95

1. A
2. F
3. C
4. H
5. A
6. F
7. C

Page 96

1. 50.24 in.²
2. 7,850 mm²
3. 7.065 in.²
4. 314 ft.²
5. 2.0096 cm²
6. 0.785 mm²
7. 1,256 mm²
8. 176.625 in.²
9. 13.8474 m²

Page 97

1. 45 cm²
2. 20 in.²
3. 10.5 ft.²
4. 5.625 m²
5. 12 yd.²

Page 98

1. B
2. F
3. C
4. J
5. D
6. F
7. B
8. F

Page 99

1. 48 cubic units
2. 40 cubic units
3. 36 cubic units
4. 42 cubic units
5. 19 cubic units
6. 28 cubic units
7. 48 cubic units
8. 25 cubic units
9. 33 cubic units

Page 100

1. 180 in.³
2. 198 mm³
3. 80 cm³
4. 216 m³
5. 20 in.³
6. 18 ft.³
7. 40 cm³
8. 50 m³
9. 1,792 ft.³

Page 101

Mini-Test 2

1. C
2. G
3. C
4. G
5. D
6. H
7. B
8. G

Page 103

1. C
2. C
3. C
4. S
5. C
6. S
7. C
8. S
9. S

Page 104

1. B
2. J
3. C
4. F
5. B

Page 105

1. variable: n (or any other letter)
   sentence:
   $3 + n = 9$
   model:

   solution: $n = 6$

2. variable: p (or any other letter)
   sentence:
   $4 + p = 13$
   model:

   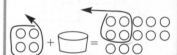

   solution: $p = 9$

Page 106

1. 1
2. 2
3. 6
4. 4
5. -4
6. 4
7. $1\dfrac{1}{2}$
8. 5
9. 11
10. 8
11. -9
12. 12

Page 107

1. D
2. H
3. B
4. H

Page 108

1.

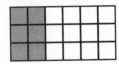

● + ● = ●●●

2.

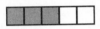

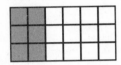

3. Check students' graphs and explanations.

Page 109
Mini-Test 3
1. B
2. Circle graph should show correct proportions.
3. F
4. C
5. J
6. C
7. J

Page 111
1. C
2. J
3. B
4. H
5. D
6. F
7. C

Page 112
1. B
2. H
3. A
4. H
5. A
6. J

Page 113
1. D
2. J
3. C
4. G
5. C
6. G

Page 114
1. B
2. F
3. D
4. G
5. C
6. J

Page 115
1. B
2. F
3. 1901–1920
4. A

Page 116
1. A
2. J
3. A
4. H
5. B

Page 117
Mini-Test 4
1. A
2. J
3. A
4. G
5. B
6. G
7. C
8. J

Pages 120–123
Final Mathematics Test
1. D
2. J
3. D
4. F
5. C
6. F
7. A

8. G
9. D
10. J
11. B
12. H
13. A
14. F
15. C
16. G
17. B
18. H
19. C
20. F
21. C
22. H
23. C
24. G
25. B
26. H
27. D

Pages 128–129
1. e
2. d
3. f
4. c
5. a
6. b
7. C
8. J
9. B
10. G
11. A
12. F
13. D
14. H
15. D
16. H
17. B
18. S–
19. S+
20. S–
21. S+
22. S+

Page 130
1. B
2. H
3. A
4. H
5. C
6. F
7. A
8. G

Pages 131–132
1. c
2. d

3. a
4. b
5. B
6. F
7. C
8. G
9. D
10. H
11. C
12. J
13. C
14. H
15. D
16. G

Pages 133–134
1. D
2. G
3. A
4. F
5. d
6. b
7. a
8. c
9. C
10. H
11. B
12. G

Pages 135–136
1. c
2. a
3. d
4. e
5. b
6. D
7. G
8. A
9. J
10. C
11. G
12. D
13. H

Pages 137–138
1. c
2. d
3. a
4. f
5. b
6. e
7. C
8. F
9. B
10. H
11. D
12. G
13. C

14. G
15. D
16. F
17. C
18. G

Page 139
1. C
2. F
3. B
4. J
5. C
6. H

Pages 140–141
1. C
2. J
3. D
4. H
5. C
6. F
7. B
8. F
9. Answers will vary, but students should indicate that television became the main form of entertainment for many families, as well as an important source of news and information. Television advertising helped create a national market for new products and fashions.
10. Answers will vary, but students should note that all three assassinations shocked and grieved the nation. The King assassination triggered riots across the country. The assassinations, riots, and protests of the 1960s made many Americans long for a return to law and order.

Page 142
1. B
2. H
3. A
4. G
5. A
6. J
7. C
8. Answers will vary, but students should mention the various uses of the personal computer in homes, schools, and businesses. Students may also mention the effect that the Internet has had on communication and the changes it has brought to the workplace, including the rise of telecommuting.

Page 143
Mini-Test 1
1. D
2. F
3. A
4. H
5. D
6. H
7. C
8. F
9. B
10. H

Page 145
1. B
2. A
3. H
4. C
5. G
6. E
7. D
8. I
9. F
10. J

Page 146
1. C
2. H
3. A
4. D
5. B
6. G
7. I
8. J
9. E
10. F

Page 147
1. D
2. F
3. C
4. G

Page 148
1. A
2. H
3. D
4. H

Page 149
Mini-Test 2
1. D
2. G
3. C
4. J

Page 151
1. C
2. J
3. Answers will vary. One possible answer: Voters have a responsibility to understand the issues and know where the candidates stand on them before voting.
4. Answers will vary. One possible answer: It benefits the accused by ensuring that he or she receives a fair trial.
5. Students' responses will vary. They are to rank the rights shown from most to least important to them personally, and then explain their rankings.

Page 152
1. C
2. J
3. D
4. F
5. A
6. H
7. C
8. G

Page 153
1. D
2. J
3. B
4. F

Page 154
1. A
2. G
3. C

Page 155
Mini-Test 3
1. A
2. J
3. D
4. J
5. A
6. G
7. C
8. J
9. D

Page 157
1. D
2. F
3. D
4. J

Page 158
1. B
2. F
3. B
4. D
5. B
6. D
7. B
8. The Speedy Bicycle Company probably builds more bicycles in a typical week. Specialization and division of

labor usually increase productivity of workers.

9. C

Page 159
1. C
2. J
3. A
4. F
5. C
6. J
7. D

Page 160
1. D
2. J
3. A
4. G
5. C

Page 161
1. B
2. J
3. B
4. J
5. B
6. J
7. N
8. S
9. L
10. N
11. L
12. L
13. S

Page 162
1. A
2. J
3. A
4. G
5. A
6. J
7. Answers will vary. Most students will conclude that people wanted to purchase the generators because they needed another source for their electricity. They were willing to pay a higher price since their normal

source of electricity was unavailable.

Page 163
1. H
2. M
3. H
4. L
5. L
6. H
7. M
8. L
9. H
10. E+
11. E
12. E+
13. E−
14. E−
15. E+
16. E
17. E−
18. E+
19. Income is closely tied to the level of education attained.

Page 164
1. C
2. G
3. B
4. J

Pages 165–166
1. **expenditures:** what things money is spent on; Record your spending habits.
   debit: spending; If you have determined your spending habits, you know what your debits are.
   credit: how much money comes in; Determine all the ways you get money.
   cash flow: the amount of money spent; You might budget a small cash flow because you

want to save for a new pair of skis.
2. (1) Record spending habits; (2) Determine debits and credits; (3) Determine cash flow and savings goal.
3. Answers will vary but should include ways the student identifies his or her expenditures, debits, credits, cash flow, and maybe savings goals.
4. Answers will vary but should incorporate the principles outlined in the passage. Debits should not exceed credits.

Page 167
Mini-Test 4
1. C
2. G
3. D
4. G
5. D
6. G
7. D
8. H

Pages 170–174
Final Social Studies Test
1. C
2. J
3. D
4. G
5. D
6. J
7. C
8. G
9. C
10. G
11. D
12. J
13. C
14. G
15. A

16. J
17. D
18. H
19. C
20. G
21. C
22. F
23. C
24. J
25. B
26. F
27. D
28. G

Page 179
1. A
2. G
3. A
4. H
5. D
6. F

Page 180
1. A
2. G
3. A
4. H
5. D
6. F
7. B

Page 181
1. A
2. F
3. A
4. G
5. C
6. H
7. A
8. F
9. B
10. J

Page 182
1. C
2. H
3. B
4. H

Page 183
Chart and graph: Answers will vary depending on the week the student does the research, but the chart should give accurate information for the chosen week. The bar graph should

be a correct representation of the data.

1. Answers will vary but should include a complete citation for the source(s).
2. Answers may vary, but students should indicate that they would consult an online or print source to verify the claim.

Page 184
1. B
2. H
3. Answers may vary. Possible answer: Lauren made accurate, detailed records of her experiment.
4. Answers may vary. Possible answer: Lauren should have either used new flashlights for both experiments or used the same old flashlights for both experiments. This would have given her a clearer idea of how long the batteries last under specific conditions.

Page 185
1. C
2. J
3. A

Page 186
1. C
2. G
3. A
4. J
5. B
6. J
7. D

Page 187
Mini-Test 1
1. B
2. H
3. A
4. Answers may vary, but students should indicate that Ryan needs to analyze the data he collected, and then draw conclusions from the data. He should decide if the conclusions support his original hypothesis. Students may also suggest that Ryan should present his findings in graph form along with his written report.
5. Answers may vary but should demonstrate that the student understands that similar scientific investigations seldom produce exactly the same results.
6. G

Pages 189–190
1. B
2. J
3. C
4. G
5. A
6. G
7. A
8. F
9. B
10. F
11. C
12. G
13. D
14. J
15. C

Page 191
Mini-Test 2
1. A
2. G
3. D
4. H
5. C
6. H
7. D
8. H
9. B
10. J

Page 193
1. B
2. H
3. C
4. G
5. C
6. F
7. D
8. H

Page 194
1. B
2. H
3. C
4. G
5. B
6. J
7. C

Page 195
1. A
2. F
3. C
4. F
5. C
6. H
7. B
8. G
9. C

Page 196
Mini-Test 3
1. C
2. J
3. B
4. H
5. A
6. H
7. D
8. J
9. D

Page 198
1. C
2. H
3. B
4. G
5. D
6. G
7. D
8. H
9. C
10. G
11. A
12. J

Page 199
1. L
2. I
3. I
4. I
5. L
6. I
7. L
8. L
9. I
10. I
11. L
12. I
13. A
14. Answers will vary, but students should mention the importance of nutrition.

Pages 200–201
1. B
2. J
3. A
4. G
5. Cell membrane
6. Cytoplasm
7. Mitochondrion
8. Nucleus
9. Cell wall
10. Chloroplast
11. Chromosomes

Page 202
1. H
2. B
3. B
4. H
5. B
6. B
7. H
8. B
9. H

10. H
11. B
12. B
13. H
14. B

Page 203
Mini-Test 4
1. C
2. G
3. C
4. J
5. A
6. F
7. B
8. G
9. A
10. J
11. B

Pages 206–209
Final Science Test
1. B
2. J
3. C
4. H
5. A
6. H
7. A
8. H
9. C
10. G
11. D
12. F
13. B
14. J
15. D
16. H
17. C
18. G
19. B
20. G
21. A
22. F
23. B
24. J
25. D
26. H
27. C
28. G
29. A

NOTES

NOTES

NOTES